Help yourself to
advanced algebra

Hugh Neill

LONGMAN

Addison Wesley Longman Ltd
Edinburgh Gate
Harlow
Essex
CM20 2JE
England and Associated Companies throughout the World

First published 1997
Produced by Longman Singapore Publishers (Pte) Ltd
Printed in Singapore

ISBN 0582 31805 X

The Publisher's policy is to use paper manufactured from sustainable forests.

Contents

Preface

The purpose of this book is to help to increase students' facility in the algebra of advanced level mathematics.

There are plenty of exercises in this book. The exercises are graded, and most types of exercise have a worked example with a full commentary to provide assistance.

I would like to thank the authors of New General Mathematics, Messrs J B Channon, A McLeish Smith and H C Head, for allowing me to use their text for some of the sections of this book, Rosemary Emanuel for checking the manuscripts and her many helpful suggestions, Sue Maunder for checking the answers and Addison Wesley Longman for their speed in producing this book.

The responsibility for any errors is mine.

Hugh Neill
March 9, 1997

1 How to use this book

Assumptions made

This is a book which is designed to help you to learn advanced algebra by giving you a number of carefully worked examples, and then problems based on them.

The assumption is that you are not a beginner, and that you have been taught this work already. Thus, no theory is given; if you need to know more, then you should consult your algebra book and your teacher.

At the beginning of each chapter, there is a list of topics which you should have studied before commencing work.

Learning a technique

Suppose that you need to learn how to carry out a particular technique. Look for the chapter which includes the technique, check that you have covered the theory, and then study the worked examples carefully, preferably with a pen in your hand.

Write down the steps as you go, and check each step carefully. Ask yourself: Why was this particular step chosen? Do I agree with the working? Why is it like that?

Remember that mathematics is not disconnected, and if you can learn the general principles behind algebra, you will make better progress in other areas of the subject.

Trying the exercises

If you get stuck with a particular exercise, then look back at a worked example similar to the one you are having difficulty with, and try to isolate the place where you are having the problem.

Look at the answer. Sometimes, but not always, the general form of the answer can give you a clue. Remember that sometimes there can be different forms of the same answer, and it may be that your answer is correct, but you do not recognise it as such.

There are plenty of exercises in the book. Do as many as you need to perfect a technique.

Short cuts

In many cases the examples are worked in more detail than you need to give in a solution. If you can skip lines, go ahead; but don't make errors by doing so! It is better to write more steps, and get the solution correct, than to skip steps, get things wrong, and subsequently lose confidence.

Answers

Answers are given, but in some cases the answer given may be in a form different from yours. If that is so, and you cannot reconcile your answer with that in the book, you should seek help.

2 Indices

You will need to know that when x and y are positive whole numbers the rules for indices are

- $a^x \times a^y = a^{x+y}$ Rule 1

- $a^x \div a^y = a^{x-y}$ Rule 2

- $\left(a^x\right)^y = a^{xy}$.   Rule 3

Meanings can also be found for powers when x and y are any numbers, positive, negative or fractions.

These rules, which won't be proved are:

- $a^{\frac{1}{n}} = \sqrt[n]{a}$ Rule 4

- $a^0 = 1$ Rule 5

- $a^{-n} = \dfrac{1}{a^n}$ Rule 6

- $a^{\frac{x}{y}} = \sqrt[y]{a^x}$ or $\left(\sqrt[y]{a}\right)^x$ Rule 7

1   Simplify $3a^2 \times 2a^4$.

This means $3 \times a^2 \times 2 \times a^4$, so multiply the numbers and then use Rule 1.

$$3a^2 \times 2a^4$$
$$= 6a^6.$$

2   Simplify $3a \times (2a)^2$.

This means $3a \times 2a \times 2a$, so multiply the numbers and then use Rule 1.

$$3a \times (2a)^2$$
$$= 12a^3.$$

3 Simplify $\dfrac{3a^{-2}}{6a^{-4}}$.

$$\dfrac{3a^{-2}}{6a^{-4}}$$

Start by looking at and cancelling the numbers.

$$= \dfrac{a^{-2}}{2a^{-4}}$$

Use Rule 6.

$$= \dfrac{\dfrac{1}{a^2}}{\dfrac{2}{a^4}}$$

Multiply the numerator and denominator of the big fraction by a^4, in the form $\dfrac{a^4}{1}$, and then cancel.

$$= \dfrac{\dfrac{1}{a^2} \times \dfrac{a^4}{1}}{\dfrac{2}{a^4} \times \dfrac{a^4}{1}} = \dfrac{\dfrac{a^2}{1}}{\dfrac{2}{1}} = \dfrac{a^2}{2}.$$

4 Simplify $25^{\frac{1}{2}}$.

$$25^{\frac{1}{2}}$$

Using Rule 4, this means $\sqrt{25}$.

$$= 5.$$

5 Simplify $16^{\frac{3}{2}}$.

$$16^{\frac{3}{2}}$$

Using Rule 7, this means $\left(\sqrt{16}\right)^3$.

$$= 4^3 = 64.$$

6 Simplify 3^{-4}.

Using Rule 6, this means $\dfrac{1}{3^4}$.

3^{-4}

$= \dfrac{1}{3^4} = \dfrac{1}{81}$.

7 Simplify $9^{-\frac{3}{2}}$.

Using Rule 6, this means $\dfrac{1}{9^{\frac{3}{2}}}$. Then use Rule 7.

$9^{-\frac{3}{2}}$

$= \dfrac{1}{9^{\frac{3}{2}}} = \dfrac{1}{3^3} = \dfrac{1}{27}$.

8 Simplify $\left(\dfrac{2}{3}\right)^{-4}$.

Using Rule 6, this means $\dfrac{1}{\left(\dfrac{2}{3}\right)^4}$.

$\left(\dfrac{2}{3}\right)^{-4}$

$= \dfrac{1}{\left(\dfrac{2}{3}\right)^4} = \dfrac{1}{\dfrac{16}{81}} = \dfrac{81}{16}$.

9 Simplify $\left(\dfrac{27}{8}\right)^{-\frac{2}{3}}$.

Use Rule 6 to obtain $\dfrac{1}{\left(\dfrac{27}{8}\right)^{\frac{2}{3}}}$.

$\left(\dfrac{27}{8}\right)^{-\frac{2}{3}}$

$= \dfrac{1}{\left(\dfrac{27}{8}\right)^{\frac{2}{3}}}$.

Use Rule 7 to simplify the denominator.	$= \dfrac{1}{\left(\sqrt[3]{\left(\dfrac{27}{8}\right)}\right)^2} = \dfrac{1}{\left(\dfrac{3}{2}\right)^2} = \dfrac{1}{\dfrac{9}{4}} = \dfrac{4}{9}.$

10 Simplify $\left(2\tfrac{1}{4}\right)^{\frac{1}{2}}$.

	$\left(2\tfrac{1}{4}\right)^{\frac{1}{2}}$
Express the number in the bracket as a fraction.	$= \left(\dfrac{9}{4}\right)^{\frac{1}{2}}.$
Use Rule 4.	$= \dfrac{3}{2}.$

11 Simplify $3x^0$.

	$3x^0$
This means $3 \times x^0$. Then use Rule 5.	$= 3 \times 1 = 3$.

Exercise 2

Simplify the following expressions.

1	$2a \times 3a^2$	**2**	$2a \times (3a)^2$
3	$(2a)^2 \times 3a$	**4**	$4^{\frac{1}{2}}$
5	$27^{\frac{1}{3}}$	**6**	$125^{\frac{1}{3}}$
7	$\sqrt[3]{2^6}$	**8**	$8^{\frac{2}{3}}$
9	2^{-2}	**10**	3^{-3}
11	$9^{\frac{1}{2}}$	**12**	$9^{-\frac{1}{2}}$
13	$\left(25a^2\right)^{\frac{1}{2}}$	**14**	$2a^{-1}$
15	$(2a)^{-1}$	**16**	$4^{\frac{3}{2}}$

17 $2^{-2} \times 2^3$

18 $\left(2^2\right)^2$

19 10^{-2}

20 $\sqrt{1\frac{9}{16}}$

21 $3a^{-2}$

22 $(3a)^{-2}$

23 $\sqrt{3^4}$

24 $\left(a^2\right)^{-\frac{1}{2}}$

25 $\left(\frac{1}{9}\right)^{-1}$

26 $\left(\frac{1}{4}\right)^{-\frac{1}{2}}$

27 $3^{\frac{1}{2}} \times 3^{\frac{3}{2}}$

28 $\left(\frac{1}{27}\right)^{-\frac{2}{3}}$

29 $3^{\frac{1}{2}} \times 3^{-\frac{3}{2}}$

30 $0.04^{\frac{1}{2}}$

31 $2a^{-1} \times 3a^2$

32 $(2a)^{-1} \times 3a^2$

33 $2a^{-1} \times (3a)^2$

34 $16^{-\frac{3}{2}}$

35 $2^{\frac{1}{2}} \times 2^{\frac{5}{2}}$

36 $\left(2^6\right)^{-\frac{2}{3}}$

37 $125^{-\frac{2}{3}}$

38 $3^x \times 3^{-x}$

39 $16^{-\frac{3}{4}}$

40 $0.027^{\frac{2}{3}}$

41 $2a \times 3a^{-2}$

42 $2a \times (3a)^{-2}$

43 $4^{-\frac{3}{2}}$

44 $\left(\frac{8}{27}\right)^{-\frac{2}{3}}$

45 $\dfrac{1}{3^{-2}}$

46 2×2^{-3}

47 $\sqrt[3]{4^{1.5}}$

48 $3^{n-1} \times 3^{1-n}$

49 $64^{-\frac{5}{6}}$

50 $\sqrt[3]{8a^{-6}}$

51 $2x^{\frac{1}{2}} \times 3x^{-\frac{5}{2}}$

52 $0.125^{-\frac{1}{3}}$

53 $\left(\frac{16}{9}\right)^{-\frac{3}{2}}$

54 $\sqrt[4]{16a^{-12}}$

55 $4a^3b \times 3ab^{-2}$

56 $4a^3b \times (3ab)^{-2}$

57 $\sqrt{\left(125^2\right)^{-\frac{1}{3}}}$

58 $\dfrac{75a^2b^{-2}}{5a^3b^{-3}}$

59 $(2x)^{\frac{1}{2}} \times \left(2x^3\right)^{\frac{3}{2}}$

60 $\left(\frac{18}{32}\right)^{-\frac{3}{2}}$

Re-write the following expressions using positive indices only.

61 a^{-2}

62 b^{-1}

63 $c^{-\frac{2}{3}}$

64 xy^{-1}

65 $(xy)^{-1}$

66 $a^{-2}b^3$

Help yourself to advanced algebra

67 ab^{-3} **68** $(ab)^{-3}$

69 $2x^{-\frac{1}{2}}$ **70** $3y^{-\frac{2}{5}}$

Solve for x the following equations.

71 $x^{\frac{1}{2}} = 2$ **72** $x^{\frac{1}{3}} = 3$

73 $x^{-1} = 2$ **74** $x^{-2} = 9$

75 $2x^3 = 54$ **76** $x^{-\frac{1}{2}} = 5$

77 $x^{-\frac{2}{3}} = 9$ **78** $2x^{-3} = -16$

79 $5x = 40x^{-\frac{1}{2}}$ **80** $x = 9\sqrt{9x^{\frac{1}{2}}}$

Simplify the following:

81 $(0.027)^{\frac{1}{3}}$ **82** $(1.44)^{-\frac{1}{2}}$

83 $\left(1\frac{7}{9}\right)^{\frac{1}{2}}$ **84** $\left(\frac{8}{27}\right)^{\frac{1}{3}}$

85 $\dfrac{2a^{-1}}{4a^{-3}}$ **86** $\dfrac{(x^2)^{-2}}{(x^3)^{-1}}$

87 $\dfrac{(xy^3)^{-1}}{(x^2y^{-1})^2}$ **88** $\dfrac{(2x^2y^2)^{\frac{1}{2}}}{(2xy^{-2})^{\frac{3}{2}}}$

3   Logarithms

You will need to know that

- the equation $m = \log_a x$ is equivalent to the equation $x = a^m$ Definition

- $\log_a(mn) = \log_a m + \log_a n$ Rule 1

- $\log_a\left(\dfrac{m}{n}\right) = \log_a m - \log_a n$ Rule 2

- $\log_a\left(m^p\right) = p\log_a m$.   Rule 3

- $\log_a a = 1$ Rule 4

- $\log_a 1 = 0$ Rule 5

- in the above equations a, m, n and x are always positive, and that p can be either positive or negative.

1   Find $\log_2 8$, $\log_9 27$ and $\log_5 0.04$.

	Let $x = \log_2 8$.
Use the definition to rewrite the equation.	Then $8 = 2^x$ so $x = 3$.
	Let $y = \log_9 27$.
Use the definition to rewrite the equation.	Then $27 = 9^y$, or $3^3 = 3^{2y}$ so $2y = 3$, or $y = 1\frac{1}{2}$.
	Let $z = \log_5 0.04$.
Use the definition to rewrite the equation.	Then $0.04 = 5^z$, or $\dfrac{1}{25} = 5^z$ so $5^{-2} = 5^z$, so $z = -2$.

2   Let $\log_{10} 2 = p$ and $\log_{10} 3 = q$. Express $\log_{10} 6$, $\log_{10} 9$ and $\log_{10} 15$ in terms of p, q and r.

Use Rule 1.	$\log_{10} 6 = \log_{10} 2 + \log_{10} 3 = p + q$.
Use Rule 3	$\log_{10} 9 = \log_{10} 3^2 = 2\log_{10} 3 = 2q$.
Start by using Rule 1.	$\log_{10} 15 = \log_{10} 3 + \log_{10} 5$.

You need to use the fact that $\log_{10} 10 = 1$, *which comes from the definition.*
From Rule 1, $\log_{10} 5 + \log_{10} 2 = \log_{10} 10 = 1$, *so* $\log_{10} 5 = 1 - \log_{10} 2 = 1 - p$.

Use $\log_{10} 5 = 1 - p$.	$\log_{10} 15 = \log_{10} 3 + \log_{10} 5$ $\qquad\qquad = q + 1 - p$.

3   Express $\log_{10} 2 + 2\log_{10} 3 - 1$ as the logarithm to the base 10 of a single number.

Use Rule 3 on $2\log_{10} 3$.	$\log_{10} 2 + 2\log_{10} 3 - 1$ $\qquad = \log_{10} 2 + \log_{10} 3^2 - 1$
Then use Rule 1.	$\qquad = \log_{10} 18 - 1$
Write 1 as $\log_{10} 10$, and then use Rule 2.	$\qquad = \log_{10} 18 - \log_{10} 10$ $\qquad = \log_{10} 1.8$.

4   Solve the equations $\log_{10} x = 2$ and $\log_3 x = 5$.

	$\log_{10} x = 2$
Rewrite this using the definition.	$10^2 = x$, so $x = 100$.

	$\log_3 x = 5$
Rewrite this using the definition.	$3^5 = x$, so $x = 243$.

5   Find $\log_3 6.62$.

	Let $x = \log_3 6.62$.
Rewrite this using the definition.	Then $3^x = 6.62$.
Take logs to the base 10.	$\log_{10} 3^x = \log_{10} 6.62$.
Use Rule 3.	$x \log_{10} 3 = \log_{10} 6.62$.
Divide both sides by $\log_{10} 3$ and evaluate.	$x = \dfrac{\log_{10} 6.62}{\log_{10} 3} \approx 1.720$.

6   Solve for x the equation $2^x = 3$.

	$2^x = 3$
Take logs to the base 10.	Then $\log_{10} 2^x = \log_{10} 3$.
Use Rule 3.	$x \log_{10} 2 = \log_{10} 3$.
Divide both sides by $\log_{10} 2$ and evaluate.	$x = \dfrac{\log_{10} 3}{\log_{10} 2} \approx 1.585$.

Exercise 3

In questions 1 to 20 evaluate the following logarithms.

1 $\log_2 4$	**2** $\log_{10} 1000$
3 $\log_5 25$	**4** $\log_3 81$
5 $\log_{12} 144$	**6** $\log_6 216$
7 $\log_7 \frac{1}{7}$	**8** $\log_4 64$

9	$\log_4 8$	**10**	$\log_8 4$
11	$\log_{25} 0.2$	**12**	$\log_{49} 7$
13	$\log_{1000} 10$	**14**	$\log_4 \frac{1}{8}$
15	$\log_{16} 0.25$	**16**	$\log_{100} 0.001$
17	$\log_9 \frac{1}{27}$	**18**	$\log_8 0.0625$
19	$\log_{1.2} 1.728$	**20**	$\log_{0.2} 25$

In questions 21 to 27, let $\log_{10} 2 = p$, $\log_{10} 3 = q$ and $\log_{10} 7 = r$. Then write the given expression in terms of p, q and r.

21	$\log_{10} 8$	**22**	$\log_{10} 49$
23	$\log_{10} 14$	**24**	$\log_{10} 42$
25	$\log_{10} 5$	**26**	$\log_{10} 35$
27	$\log_{10} 0.75$	**28**	$\log_{10} 1.2$

In questions 29 to 34, express the given expression as the logarithm to the base 10 of a single number or the logarithm to the base 10 of a fraction. All the logarithms are to the base 10.

29	$\log 3 + \log 4$	**30**	$\log 4 - \log 3$
31	$3 \log 5$	**32**	$\frac{1}{2} \log 25$
33	$-\log 3$	**34**	$1 + \log 3$

In questions 35 to 38, solve the given equations for x.

35	$\log_{10} x = 3$	**36**	$\log_{10} x = -2$
37	$\log_x 81 = 4$	**38**	$2 \log_x \left(\frac{27}{8}\right) = 6$

In questions 39 to 42, simplify the following expressions, all the logarithms being to the base 10.

39	$\dfrac{\log 4}{\log 2}$	**40**	$\dfrac{\log 16}{\log 8}$
41	$\dfrac{\log \sqrt{3}}{\log 9}$	**42**	$\dfrac{\log 0.2}{\log 5}$

Rewrite the equations in questions 43 to 48 in index form.

43	$\log_a x = b$	**44**	$\log_a x + \log_a y = 1$
45	$\log_a x + 1 = 0$	**46**	$\log_a x + 2 \log_a y = 3$
47	$\log_a x - \log_a y = \log_a z$	**48**	$2 \log_a x - 3 \log_a y = 4 \log_a z$

In questions 49 to 56, calculate the following logarithms, giving your answer correct to 3 decimal places.

49 $\log_2 5$ **50** $\log_7 6$

51 $\log_5 2.64$ **52** $\log_3 2$

53 $\log_5 12$ **54** $\log_3 80$

55 $\log_{0.5} 3$ **56** $\log_{0.1} 2$

Solve for x the following equations, giving your answer correct to 3 decimal places.

57 $10^x = 3$ **58** $3^x = 10$

59 $5^x = 100$ **60** $6^x = 120$

61 $4^x = 0.88$ **62** $0.2^x = 0.8$

63 $2^{-x} = 5$ **64** $3^{-2x} = 0.7$

4   Surds

You will need to know that

● $\sqrt{mn} = \sqrt{m} \times \sqrt{n}$ Rule 1

● $\sqrt{\dfrac{m}{n}} = \dfrac{\sqrt{m}}{\sqrt{n}}$ Rule 2

1   Simplify $\sqrt{8}$.

Look for perfect squares under the square root sign.	$\sqrt{8} = \sqrt{4 \times 2}$.
Use Rule 1.	$= \sqrt{4} \times \sqrt{2}$ $= 2\sqrt{2}$.

2   Simplify $\sqrt{27} \times \sqrt{50}$.

Look for perfect squares under the square root signs.	$\sqrt{27} \times \sqrt{50} = \sqrt{9 \times 3} \times \sqrt{25 \times 2}$.
Use Rule 1, and then use Rule 1 again.	$= 3\sqrt{3} \times 5\sqrt{2}$ $= 15\sqrt{6}$.

3   Simplify $\sqrt{12} \times 3\sqrt{60} \times \sqrt{45}$.

	$\sqrt{12} \times 3\sqrt{60} \times \sqrt{45}$
Look for perfect squares under the square root signs, and then use Rule 1 again and again.	$= \sqrt{4 \times 3} \times 3\sqrt{4 \times 15} \times \sqrt{9 \times 5}$ $= 2\sqrt{3} \times 6\sqrt{15} \times 3\sqrt{5}$ $= 36\sqrt{3 \times 15 \times 5}$ $= 36 \times 15 = 540$.

4   Simplify $3\sqrt{50} - 5\sqrt{32} + 4\sqrt{8}$.

$$3\sqrt{50} - 5\sqrt{32} + 4\sqrt{8}$$

Look for perfect squares under the square root signs, and then use Rule 1 again and again.

$$= 3\sqrt{25 \times 2} - 5\sqrt{16 \times 2} + 4\sqrt{4 \times 2}$$
$$= 15\sqrt{2} - 20\sqrt{2} + 8\sqrt{2}$$
$$= 3\sqrt{2}.$$

When a surd appears in the denominator, it is usually a good idea to remove it by a process called rationalisation. The essential idea is to multiply both numerator and denominator by a surd which removes the surd from the denominator and thus makes the denominator rational, (often called rationalising the denominator).

5   Simplify $\dfrac{6}{\sqrt{3}}$.

Multiply numerator and denominator by $\sqrt{3}$.

$$\frac{6}{\sqrt{3}} = \frac{6}{\sqrt{3}} \times \frac{\sqrt{3}}{\sqrt{3}} = \frac{6\sqrt{3}}{3} = 2\sqrt{3}.$$

6   Simplify $\dfrac{5\sqrt{7} \times 2\sqrt{3}}{\sqrt{45} \times \sqrt{21}}$.

$$\frac{5\sqrt{7} \times 2\sqrt{3}}{\sqrt{45} \times \sqrt{21}}$$

Look for perfect squares under the square root signs. Cancel the $\sqrt{7}$ and the $\sqrt{3}$.

$$= \frac{5\sqrt{7} \times 2\sqrt{3}}{\sqrt{9 \times 5} \times \sqrt{7} \times \sqrt{3}}$$

Use Rule 1 in the denominator.

$$= \frac{5 \times 2}{3\sqrt{5}}$$

15

Multiply numerator and denominator by $\sqrt{5}$, and simplify the result.	$= \dfrac{5 \times 2}{3\sqrt{5}} \times \dfrac{\sqrt{5}}{\sqrt{5}}$ $= \dfrac{2\sqrt{5}}{3}.$

7 Simplify $\dfrac{1}{\sqrt{2}-1}$ by rationalising the denominator.

The method used to remove the surd from the denominator relies on the use of the difference of two squares formula $a^2 - b^2 = (a+b)(a-b)$. *In this example,* $\left(\sqrt{2}+1\right)\left(\sqrt{2}-1\right) = \left(\sqrt{2}\right)^2 - 1^2 = 2 - 1 = 1.$

Multiply numerator and denominator by $\sqrt{2}+1$ and simplify the result.	$\dfrac{1}{\sqrt{2}-1} = \dfrac{1}{\sqrt{2}-1} \times \dfrac{\sqrt{2}+1}{\sqrt{2}+1}$ $= \dfrac{\sqrt{2}+1}{2-1} = \sqrt{2}+1.$

8 Simplify $\dfrac{2+5\sqrt{2}}{5-3\sqrt{2}}$ by rationalising the denominator.

	$\dfrac{2+5\sqrt{2}}{5-3\sqrt{2}}$
Multiply numerator and denominator by $5+3\sqrt{2}$ and simplify the result.	$= \dfrac{2+5\sqrt{2}}{5-3\sqrt{2}} \times \dfrac{5+3\sqrt{2}}{5+3\sqrt{2}}$ $= \dfrac{10 + 6\sqrt{2} + 25\sqrt{2} + 30}{25 - 18}$ $= \dfrac{31\sqrt{2} + 40}{7}.$

Exercise 4

In questions 1 to 16, express each of the following as the square root of a single number.

1	$2\sqrt{3}$	**2**	$3\sqrt{2}$
3	$2\sqrt{2}$	**4**	$3\sqrt{3}$
5	$5\sqrt{2}$	**6**	$3\sqrt{5}$
7	$2\sqrt{7}$	**8**	$4\sqrt{6}$
9	$6\sqrt{3}$	**10**	$5\sqrt{5}$
11	$10\sqrt{3}$	**12**	$3\sqrt{10}$
13	$2\sqrt{11}$	**14**	$3\sqrt{8}$
15	$5\sqrt{7}$	**16**	$2\sqrt{2} \times 3\sqrt{3}$

In questions 17 to 30 simplify the given expression by making the number under the square root sign as small as possible.

17	$\sqrt{20}$	**18**	$\sqrt{32}$
19	$\sqrt{48}$	**20**	$\sqrt{75}$
21	$\sqrt{72}$	**22**	$\sqrt{24}$
23	$\sqrt{63}$	**24**	$\sqrt{54}$
25	$\sqrt{200}$	**26**	$\sqrt{84}$
27	$\sqrt{99}$	**28**	$\sqrt{150}$
29	$\sqrt{98}$	**30**	$\sqrt{288}$

In questions 31 to 44, simplify the given expression.

31	$\sqrt{5} \times \sqrt{10}$	**32**	$\sqrt{8} \times \sqrt{2}$
33	$\sqrt{2} \times \sqrt{6} \times \sqrt{3}$	**34**	$\sqrt{30} \times \sqrt{5}$
35	$\sqrt{12} \times \sqrt{3}$	**36**	$\left(4\sqrt{3}\right)^2$
37	$\left(\sqrt{2}\right)^3$	**38**	$\sqrt{15} \times \sqrt{12}$
39	$\sqrt{32} \times \sqrt{12}$	**40**	$\left(\sqrt{3}\right)^5$
41	$\left(2\sqrt{7}\right)^2$	**42**	$\sqrt{10} \times 3\sqrt{2} \times \sqrt{20}$
43	$\sqrt{5} \times \sqrt{24} \times \sqrt{30}$	**44**	$\sqrt{6} \times \sqrt{8} \times \sqrt{10} \times \sqrt{12}$

In questions 45 to 60, simplify the given expression by rationalising the denominator.

45	$\dfrac{1}{\sqrt{2}}$	**46**	$\dfrac{2}{\sqrt{2}}$

47 $\dfrac{6}{\sqrt{2}}$

48 $\dfrac{10}{\sqrt{5}}$

49 $\dfrac{4}{\sqrt{8}}$

50 $\dfrac{21}{\sqrt{6}}$

51 $\dfrac{15}{\sqrt{3}}$

52 $\sqrt{\dfrac{4}{5}}$

53 $\sqrt{\dfrac{9}{7}}$

54 $\dfrac{21}{\sqrt{7}}$

55 $\dfrac{2\sqrt{3}}{\sqrt{6}}$

56 $\dfrac{8}{\sqrt{18}}$

57 $\sqrt{\dfrac{12}{50}}$

58 $\dfrac{3\sqrt{2}}{\sqrt{10}}$

59 $\dfrac{30}{\sqrt{75}}$

60 $\dfrac{30}{\sqrt{72}}$

In questions 61 to 74, simplify the given expression.

61 $\sqrt{12} + \sqrt{3}$

62 $3\sqrt{2} - \sqrt{18}$

63 $\sqrt{175} - 4\sqrt{7}$

64 $\sqrt{45} + 3\sqrt{20} - 8\sqrt{5}$

65 $\sqrt{99} - \sqrt{44} - \sqrt{11}$

66 $2\sqrt{8} - 3\sqrt{32} + 4\sqrt{50}$

67 $2\sqrt{150} - \sqrt{96} - 2\sqrt{24}$

68 $2\sqrt{54} + \sqrt{24} - \sqrt{216}$

69 $3\sqrt{28} - 5\sqrt{63} + 4\sqrt{112}$

70 $\dfrac{\sqrt{18} \times \sqrt{20} \times \sqrt{24}}{\sqrt{8} \times \sqrt{30}}$

71 $\dfrac{\sqrt{3} \times \sqrt{8} \times \sqrt{39}}{\sqrt{24} \times \sqrt{26}}$

72 $\sqrt{3} + \dfrac{1}{\sqrt{3}} - \dfrac{1}{\sqrt{27}}$

73 $2\sqrt{2} + \dfrac{3}{\sqrt{2}} + \dfrac{4}{\sqrt{8}}$

74 $\dfrac{12}{\sqrt{24} - \sqrt{6}}$

In questions 75 to 90, simplify the given expression by rationalising the denominator.

75 $\dfrac{1}{2 - \sqrt{3}}$

76 $\dfrac{1}{2 + \sqrt{3}}$

77 $\dfrac{1}{\sqrt{3} - \sqrt{2}}$

78 $\dfrac{1}{\sqrt{3} + \sqrt{2}}$

79 $\dfrac{3 - \sqrt{2}}{3 + \sqrt{2}}$

80 $\dfrac{3 - \sqrt{2}}{3 + 2\sqrt{2}}$

81 $\dfrac{1}{2\sqrt{5}-3\sqrt{2}}$

82 $\dfrac{\sqrt{7}-\sqrt{3}}{3\sqrt{3}+2\sqrt{7}}$

83 $\dfrac{1}{\sqrt{5}-\sqrt{3}}+\sqrt{5}+\sqrt{3}$

84 $\dfrac{\sqrt{5}-\sqrt{2}}{\sqrt{2}+2\sqrt{5}}$

85 $\dfrac{\sqrt{8}+\sqrt{2}}{\sqrt{8}-\sqrt{2}}$

86 $\dfrac{\sqrt{6}+\sqrt{2}}{\sqrt{6}+2\sqrt{2}}$

87 $\dfrac{\sqrt{6}+\sqrt{2}}{\sqrt{6}-\sqrt{2}}$

88 $\dfrac{\sqrt{12}-\sqrt{3}}{\sqrt{12}+\sqrt{3}}$

89 $\dfrac{\sqrt{a}-\sqrt{b}}{\sqrt{a}+\sqrt{b}}$

90 $\dfrac{\sqrt{n+1}+\sqrt{n}}{\sqrt{n+1}-\sqrt{n}}$

5 Simultaneous equations, one linear and one quadratic

You will need to know

- how to eliminate a variable between two equations

- how to solve a quadratic equation by factorising.

1 Solve the simultaneous equations
$$x^2 + y^2 = 5$$
$$x + y = 1$$

From the linear equation, either find x in terms of y, or y in terms of x, whichever is simpler.	From $x + y = 1$, $x = 1 - y$.
Substitute in the other equation, and simplify by removing brackets, collecting terms and dividing by any common factor which is not zero.	$(1 - y)^2 + y^2 = 5$ $1 - 2y + y^2 + y^2 = 5$ $2y^2 - 2y - 4 = 0$ $y^2 - y - 2 = 0$.
Solve the quadratic equation by factorising.	$(y + 1)(y - 2) = 0$ so $y = -1$ or 2.
Find the corresponding values of x, and present the solutions.	When $y = -1$, $x = 2$, and when $y = 2$, $x = -1$, so the solutions are $x = -1$, $y = 2$ and $x = 2$, $y = -1$.

2 Solve the simultaneous equations
$$x^2 + y^2 = 25$$
$$7x + y = 25$$

In this example, it is much easier to find y in terms of x than the other way round.	From $7x + y = 25$, $y = 25 - 7x$.

20

Substitute in the other equation, and simplify by removing brackets, collecting terms and dividing by any common factor which is not zero.	$x^2 + (25 - 7x)^2 = 25$ $x^2 + 625 - 350x + 49x^2 = 25$ $50x^2 - 350x + 600 = 0$ $x^2 - 7x + 12 = 0.$
Solve the quadratic equation.	$(x - 3)(x - 4) = 0$ so $x = 3$ or 4.
Find the corresponding values of y, and present the solutions.	When $x = 3$, $y = 4$, and when $x = 4$, $y = -3$, so the solutions are $x = 3$, $y = 4$ and $x = 4$, $y = -3$.

3   Solve the simultaneous equations $\dfrac{1}{x} + \dfrac{2}{y} = 8$

$$3x + 5y = 3$$

Two solutions to this equation are given. The first involves fractions and gets messy. You should probably prefer the second solution.

Note that the first equation is quadratic. If you multiply both sides by xy you get $y + 2x = 8xy$.

Find x in terms of y.	$x = \dfrac{3 - 5y}{3}.$
Multiply both sides of the other equation by xy.	$y + 2x = 8xy.$
Substitute for x.	$y + 2\left(\dfrac{3 - 5y}{3}\right) = 8\left(\dfrac{3 - 5y}{3}\right)y.$
Multiply both sides by 3.	$3y + 2(3 - 5y) = 8(3 - 5y)y.$

Multiply out the brackets and simplify.	$3y + 6 - 10y = 24y - 40y^2$ $40y^2 - 31y + 6 = 0$.
Factorise and solve.	$(5y - 2)(8y - 3) = 0$ so $y = \frac{2}{5}$ or $\frac{3}{8}$.
Find the corresponding values of x, and present the solutions.	When $y = \frac{2}{5}$, $x = \frac{1}{3}$ and when $y = \frac{3}{8}$, $x = \frac{3}{8}$, so the solutions are $x = \frac{1}{3}$, $y = \frac{2}{5}$ and $x = \frac{3}{8}$, $y = \frac{3}{8}$.

4 Solve the simultaneous equations
$$\frac{1}{x} + \frac{2}{y} = 8$$
$$3x + 5y = 3$$

In this example, it may be easier to find x in terms of y, but do not divide by the 3.	$3x = 3 - 5y$.
Multiply both sides of the other equation by xy, and then multiply it by 3 in order to make the substitution easier.	$y + 2x = 8xy$ $3y + 6x = 24xy$.
Substitute for $3x$, simplify and solve the resulting quadratic equation.	$3y + 2(3x) = 8y(3x)$ $3y + 2(3 - 5y) = 8y(3 - 5y)$ $3y + 6 - 10y = 24y - 40y^2$ $40y^2 - 31y + 6 = 0$ $(5y - 2)(8y - 3) = 0$ so $y = \frac{2}{5}$ or $\frac{3}{8}$.
Find the corresponding values of x, and present the solutions.	When $y = \frac{2}{5}$, $x = \frac{1}{3}$ and when $y = \frac{3}{8}$, $x = \frac{3}{8}$, so the solutions are $x = \frac{1}{3}$, $y = \frac{2}{5}$ and $x = \frac{3}{8}$, $y = \frac{3}{8}$.

Exercise 5

Solve the following pairs of simultaneous equations.

1 $\left.\begin{array}{l} 3x^2 - 4y = -1 \\ 2x - y = 1 \end{array}\right\}$

2 $\left.\begin{array}{l} x^2 + y^2 = 34 \\ x + y = 2 \end{array}\right\}$

3 $\left.\begin{array}{l} 2x^2 + y^2 = 19 \\ x + 3y = 0 \end{array}\right\}$

4 $\left.\begin{array}{l} 9y^2 + 8x = 12 \\ 2x + 3y = 4 \end{array}\right\}$

5 $\left.\begin{array}{l} xy + 3x = 3 \\ 3x + y = 7 \end{array}\right\}$

6 $\left.\begin{array}{l} x^2 - y^2 = 27 \\ x + y = 3 \end{array}\right\}$

7 $\left.\begin{array}{l} x^2 - 4y^2 = 9 \\ x + 2y = 1 \end{array}\right\}$

8 $\left.\begin{array}{l} 4x^2 - y^2 = 15 \\ 2x - y = 5 \end{array}\right\}$

9 $\left.\begin{array}{l} 4x^2 - 9y^2 = 19 \\ 2x + 3y = 1 \end{array}\right\}$

10 $\left.\begin{array}{l} 5x^2 - 3xy = 9 \\ 5x - 3y = 3 \end{array}\right\}$

11 $\left.\begin{array}{l} 3x^2 - xy = 0 \\ 2y - 5x = 1 \end{array}\right\}$

12 $\left.\begin{array}{l} 3x - 4y = 2 \\ xy = 2 \end{array}\right\}$

13 $\left.\begin{array}{l} x^2 - xy + 8 = 0 \\ 2x - y = 2 \end{array}\right\}$

14 $\left.\begin{array}{l} x^2 - 6y^2 = 10 \\ x + 2y = 2 \end{array}\right\}$

15 $\left.\begin{array}{l} x^2 + 4y^2 = 65 \\ x + 2y = 3 \end{array}\right\}$

16 $\left.\begin{array}{l} x^2 - y = 13 \\ x - y = 11 \end{array}\right\}$

17 $\left.\begin{array}{l} xy + 3 = 0 \\ 2x + y = 1 \end{array}\right\}$

18 $\left.\begin{array}{l} xy = 6 \\ 2x - 5y = 7 \end{array}\right\}$

19 $\left.\begin{array}{l} 3x^2 - y^2 = 2 \\ 3x + 2y + 1 = 0 \end{array}\right\}$

20 $\left.\begin{array}{l} xy + 6 = 0 \\ 2x - 3y + 15 = 0 \end{array}\right\}$

21 $\left.\begin{array}{l} 3x^2 - 5xy = 8 \\ 5y - 2x = 2 \end{array}\right\}$

22 $\left.\begin{array}{l} xy + 2x^2 = 3 \\ 3x + 2y = 1 \end{array}\right\}$

23 $\left.\begin{array}{l} xy + 5x - 2y - 10 = 0 \\ 2x + y = 1 \end{array}\right\}$

24 $\left.\begin{array}{l} 2x^2 + 3xy - 2y^2 = 8 \\ 2x - y = 1 \end{array}\right\}$

25 $\left.\begin{array}{l} (x + 2y)(x - y) = 18 \\ x - 2y = 2 \end{array}\right\}$

26 $\left.\begin{array}{l} 4x^2 + 2xy - 3y^2 = 12 \\ 2x - 3y = 12 \end{array}\right\}$

27 $\left.\begin{array}{l} \dfrac{1}{y} - \dfrac{1}{x} = \dfrac{1}{60} \\ 3y - 2x = 6 \end{array}\right\}$

28 $\left.\begin{array}{l} 4x^2 + 2xy - y^2 = 1 \\ 4x + 3y = 1 \end{array}\right\}$

6 Quadratic inequalities

You will need to know

● the rules for manipulating inequalities, including the rule that multiplying or dividing both sides of an inequality by a negative number reverses the direction of the inequality

● the shape of the graph of a quadratic function of the form $y = ax^2 + bx + c$, where $a > 0$

● the meaning of $|x|$, namely that if $x \geq 0$ then $|x| = x$, and if $x < 0$ then $|x| = -x$. Note that for all values of x, that $|x|^2 = x^2$.

The strategy for solving inequalities is to think about the graph of the quadratic function and where it meets the x-axis. If $a > 0$, the graph must take one of the three forms shown in Fig. 6.1, where the horizontal line shows the position of the x-axis.

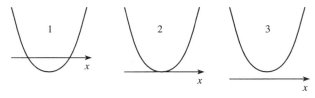

Fig. 6.1

The graph either cuts the x-axis as in case 1, touches the x axis, as in case 2, or does not cut the x-axis, as in case 3.

1   Solve the inequality $(x-3)(x-5) > 0$.

> *As $a > 0$ the graph of $y = (x-3)(x-5)$ is of type 1 in Fig. 6.1 and cuts the x-axis at $x = 3$ and $x = 5$. You can see that $y > 0$, or $(x-3)(x-5) > 0$, when the graph is above the x-axis, which is when $x < 3$ or when $x > 5$.*

Decide on the shape of the graph, and make a rough sketch of part of it.

Fig. 6.2

From Fig. 6.2, $(x-3)(x-5)>0$
when $x<3$ or when $x>5$.

2 Solve the inequality $2 \le 3x - x^2$.

Simplify the equation by subtracting 2 from both sides.

$0 \le 3x - x^2 - 2$.

Re-write the inequality so that the x^2 term is on the left and positive. Factorise if possible.

$x^2 - 3x + 2 \le 0$
$(x-1)(x-2) \le 0$.

Decide on the shape of the graph, and make a rough sketch of part of it.

Fig. 6.3

From Fig. 6.3, $(x-1)(x-2) \le 0$ when x lies between the roots, that is, when $x \ge 1$ and $x \le 2$.

You can re-write $x \ge 1$ and $x \le 2$ as a combined inequality in the form $1 \le x \le 2$, but do this only if you are sure of what you are doing.

Note that $1 \le x \le 2$ is just one part of the number line shown in Fig. 6.4.

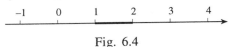

Fig. 6.4

However, note that the pair of inequalities $x \le 1$ and $x \ge 2$ refer to two parts of the number line, and cannot be written as a combined inequality. See Fig. 6.5.

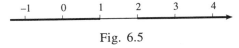

Fig. 6.5

3   Solve the inequality $\dfrac{3}{x} \geq 2$.

This does not look like a quadratic inequality - yet. It needs simplifying, and it is tempting to start by multiplying by x. However, you don't know whether x is positive or negative, so you have to tackle these cases separately.

It is better to multiply by the square of the denominator, because perfect squares can never be negative; the direction of the inequality therefore does not change. However, remember in this case, that x cannot be equal to 0.

Simplify the inequality by multiplying both sides by x^2.	$3x \geq 2x^2$.
Re-write the inequality so that the x^2 term is on the left and positive. Factorise if possible.	$2x^2 - 3x \leq 0$ $x(2x-3) \leq 0$.
Make a rough sketch of part of the graph.	

Fig. 6.6

From Fig. 6.6, $x(2x-3) \leq 0$ when x lies between the roots, that is, when $x \geq 0$ and $x \leq 1\tfrac{1}{2}$, or $0 \leq x \leq 1\tfrac{1}{2}$.

However, remember in this case, that x cannot be equal to 0.	Since $x \neq 0$, $0 < x \leq 1\tfrac{1}{2}$.

4   Solve the inequality $\dfrac{1}{x} > \dfrac{1}{x-1}$.

Simplify by multiplying both sides by $x^2(x-1)^2$. Note that $x \neq 0$ and $x \neq 1$.	$\dfrac{1}{x} \times x^2(x-1)^2 > \dfrac{1}{x-1} \times x^2(x-1)^2$ $x(x-1)^2 > x^2(x-1)$.
Collect the terms of the inequality on the left, and simplify the result by factorising. Note that $x(x-1)$ is a common factor.	$x(x-1)^2 - x^2(x-1) > 0$ $x(x-1)\{(x-1)-x\} > 0$ $x(x-1) \times (-1) > 0$.
Re-write the inequality so that the x^2 term is on the left and positive.	$x(x-1) < 0$.
Make a rough sketch of part of the graph.	

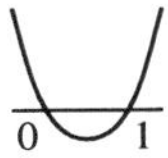

Fig. 6.7

From Fig. 6.7, $x(x-1) < 0$ when x lies between the roots, that is, when $x > 0$ and $x < 1$, or $0 < x < 1$.

5 Solve the inequality $2|x| > |x-1|$.

Two methods are given, a graphical one, and a non-graphical one. Solve the inequality graphically if you can. It is much easier.

Sketch the graph of $y = 2|x| - |x-1|$ on a graphics calculator; you may have to write $y = 2\,\mathrm{abs}\,x - \mathrm{abs}\,(x-1)$.	

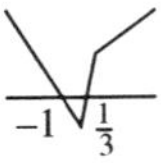

Fig. 6.8

Find where the graph intersects the x-axis.	From Fig. 6.8, $2|x| > |x-1|$ when x lies outside the roots, that is, when $x < -1$ or $x > \frac{1}{3}$.

27

6   Solve the inequality $2|x| > |x-1|$.

Solving this inequality is awkward. You need to consider the different possibilities for $|x|$ and $|x-1|$.

Suppose first that $x < 0$.	When $x < 0$, $|x| = -x$ and $|x-1| = 1-x$. Therefore $2(-x) > 1-x$ which simplifies to $x < -1$. Therefore if $x < 0$, it follows that $x < -1$, so $x < -1$ satisfies the inequality.
Suppose that $0 \le x \le 1$.	When $0 \le x \le 1$, $|x| = x$ and $|x-1| = 1-x$. Therefore $2x > 1-x$, so $3x > 1$ or $x > \frac{1}{3}$. So, if $0 \le x \le 1$, $x > \frac{1}{3}$, so $\frac{1}{3} < x \le 1$ satisfies the inequality.
Suppose that $x > 1$.	When $x > 1$, $|x| = x$ and $|x-1| = x-1$. Therefore $2x > x-1$, so $x > -1$. So, if $x > 1$, $x > -1$ so $x > 1$ satisfies the inequality.
Put these three pieces together.	$2|x| > |x-1|$ when $x < -1$ or $x > \frac{1}{3}$.

Exercise 6

Solve the following inequalities.

1	$(x-5)(x-2) > 0$	**2**	$(x+2)(x-5) < 0$
3	$(x+2)(x+3) < 0$	**4**	$(x+2)(x-5) > 0$
5	$x^2 - 36 > 0$	**6**	$x^2 < 100$
7	$(x+2)(x-3) < 0$	**8**	$(x-4)(x+1) > 0$
9	$2x^2 \ge 32$	**10**	$x^2 > x+12$
11	$x^2 + 4x \le 12$	**12**	$2x^2 + 7x \ge 4$

13 $\quad 2x^2 < x+6$

14 $\quad 4x^2 + 4x \geq 15$

15 $\quad 4x^2 + 4x \leq 0$

16 $\quad (2x-1)(x-2) \leq -x$

17 $\quad \dfrac{6}{x} < 2$

18 $\quad \dfrac{10}{x} \geq 5$

19 $\quad \dfrac{6}{x} > -2$

20 $\quad 18 \leq \dfrac{3}{x}$

21 $\quad \dfrac{24}{x} < -6$

22 $\quad \dfrac{2}{x} < \dfrac{5}{x} + 2$

23 $\quad \dfrac{1}{x-1} < \dfrac{2}{2x-1}$

24 $\quad \dfrac{2}{2x+3} < \dfrac{3}{3x-4}$

25 $\quad |x| > |x+1| - 1$

26 $\quad 2|x-1| > 3|x|$

27 $\quad |2x-1| > 2|x|$

28 $\quad |x-2| + |x-1| \geq 2$

29 $\quad |2x-1| + |1-x| \leq 5$

30 $\quad 2|x-1| + |1+x| \leq 5$

31 $\quad |x-1| + |1+x| < 2$

32 $\quad |x-1| + |1+x| - 2|x| \leq 4$

7   The discriminant

You will need to know

- the formula for solving the equation $ax^2 + bx + c = 0$

- the significance of the discriminant $b^2 - 4ac$ for determining the number of roots of the quadratic equation

- that if $b^2 - 4ac > 0$ the equation $ax^2 + bx + c = 0$ has two distinct real roots

- that if $b^2 - 4ac = 0$ the equation $ax^2 + bx + c = 0$ has one real root, sometimes described as two coincident real roots

- that if $b^2 - 4ac < 0$ the equation $ax^2 + bx + c = 0$ has no real roots.

1   Determine whether the equation $3x^2 - 7x + 5 = 0$ has 0, 1 or 2 roots.

Find the discriminant of the equation.	The value of '$b^2 - 4ac$' is $7^2 - 4 \times 3 \times 5 = 49 - 60 = -11$.
Use the sign of the discriminant to tell you about the number of roots.	As the discriminant is negative, there are no roots.

2   Find the values of k for which the equation $3x^2 - 2x - k = 0$ has 0, 1 or 2 roots.

Find the discriminant of the equation.	The value of '$b^2 - 4ac$' is $4 - 4 \times 3 \times (-k) = 4 + 12k$.
If the discriminant is positive, there will be two roots; if negative no roots; and if zero, one root (repeated).	If $4 + 12k > 0$, there will be two roots, that is, if $k > -\frac{1}{3}$. If $4 + 12k < 0$, there will be no roots, that is, if $k < -\frac{1}{3}$. And if $k = -\frac{1}{3}$ there will be one root.

3   For what value of k does the equation $(k-1)x^2 - 3x + 4(1+k) = 0$ have equal roots?

Find the discriminant of the equation.	The value of '$b^2 - 4ac$' is $9 - 4 \times (k-1) \times 4(1+k) = 25 - 16k^2$.
The roots will be equal if the discriminant is zero.	The roots will be equal if $25 - 16k^2 = 0$, that is $k = \pm\frac{5}{4}$.

4   The straight line $x + 2y = k$ is a tangent to the ellipse $3x^2 + 4y^2 = 9$. Find the possible values of k.

The strategy for this question is to start as if to solve these two equations simultaneously, and then to say that the line is a tangent if the resulting quadratic equation has equal roots.

Substitute for x using $x = k - 2y$ and rearrange the resulting equation as a quadratic equation in y.	$3(k-2y)^2 + 4y^2 = 9$ $3k^2 - 12ky + 12y^2 + 4y^2 = 9$ $16y^2 - 12ky + (3k^2 - 9) = 0$.
The roots will be equal if the discriminant is zero.	The roots will be equal if $144k^2 - 4 \times 16 \times (3k^2 - 9) = 0$.
Simplify this equation and solve it for k.	$144k^2 - 192k^2 + 576 = 0$ $-48k^2 + 576 = 0$ $k^2 = 12$ so $k = \pm\sqrt{12}$.
Present the results.	The lines $x + 2y = \pm\sqrt{12}$ are tangents to the ellipse $3x^2 + 4y^2 = 9$.

Exercise 7

In questions 1 to 8, without solving the equation, determine whether it has 0 1 or 2 roots.

1	$x^2 + 2x + 2 = 0$	**2**	$x^2 - 3x - 5 = 0$
3	$2x^2 - 12x + 18 = 0$	**4**	$2x^2 + 4x + 5 = 0$
5	$x^2 + 4 = 4x$	**6**	$3x^2 - 2x = 3$
7	$x^2 + 5x = -7$	**8**	$2x^2 + 9x = 9$

In questions 9 to 14, each equation has two roots. Determine the range of possible values of k.

9	$2x^2 - 3x + k = 0$	**10**	$kx^2 - 4x + 2 = 0$
11	$2x^2 - kx + 8 = 0$	**12**	$3x^2 + 2 = kx$
13	$(k-2)x^2 - 2kx + (k+4) = 0$	**14**	$x^2 + 3x + 2 = k(x+1)$

In questions 15 to 20, find the value or values of k such that the given equation has just 1 root.

15	$kx^2 - 3x + 2 = 0$	**16**	$x^2 - x + 1 = kx$
17	$kx^2 = 2x - 3$	**18**	$7x^2 - 2(2k+1)x + (3k-2) = 0$
19	$x^2 + 3x = kx$	**20**	$x^2 + 3x + 4 = kx$

In each of the given pair of simultaneous equations in questions 21 to 26, find the value of k (if there is one) such that the line is a tangent to the curve.

21 $\left.\begin{array}{l} 3x^2 + 4y^2 = 16 \\ -3x + 2y = k \end{array}\right\}$ **22** $\left.\begin{array}{l} 2x^2 - 3y^2 = 6 \\ x - y = k \end{array}\right\}$

23 $\left.\begin{array}{l} y^2 = 4x \\ y = k(x+1) \end{array}\right\}$ **24** $\left.\begin{array}{l} 2x^2 - 3xy + 2y^2 = 8 \\ 3x - 8 = ky \end{array}\right\}$

25 $\left.\begin{array}{l} x^2 - y^2 = 16 \\ x - y = k \end{array}\right\}$ **26** $\left.\begin{array}{l} y = x^2 - 3x + 1 \\ y = kx \end{array}\right\}$

27 Show that there is no value of k such that the line $y - 1 = kx$ is a tangent to the curve $y = x^2$.

28 Prove that if $c^2 = b^2 + a^2m^2$, then the line $y = mx + c$ is a tangent to the ellipse $\dfrac{x^2}{a^2} + \dfrac{y^2}{b^2} = 1$.

8   Arithmetic progressions

You will need to know

- that an arithmetic progression (AP) is a sequence of the form $a, a+d, a+2d, \ldots$ where a is the first term, and each term is obtained from the previous one by adding the constant difference d

- the formula $a+(n-1)d$ for the nth term of the AP

- that the sum S_n of the first n terms of an AP is $S_n = \frac{1}{2}n\{2a+(n-1)d\}$

- that the last term l of an AP with n terms is $l = a+(n-1)d$

- that the sum S_n of the first n terms of an AP is $S_n = \frac{1}{2}n(a+l)$.

The key to solving problems about arithmetic progressions is to put given information into equations containing a, d and possibly n. Then solve these equations and use the results to derive any other information that you need.

1   The first term of an arithmetic progression is 3, and the common difference is 2. Find the fifth term, the nth term, the sum to 20 terms and the sum to n terms.

The first term $a = 3$, and the common difference $d = 2$. Use the formula for the nth term of an AP with $n = 5$.	The fifth term is $a+4d = 3+4\times 2$ $\qquad = 11.$
Use the formula for the nth term of an AP.	The nth term is $a+(n-1)d = 3+2(n-1)$ $\qquad\qquad\quad = 3+2n-2 = 2n+1.$
Use the formula $\frac{1}{2}n\{2a+(n-1)d\}$ for the sum of an AP, with $a = 3$, $d = 2$ and $n = 20$.	The sum to 20 terms is $\frac{1}{2}\times 20\{2\times 3+2(20-1)\}$ $\qquad = 10\{6+38\} = 440.$

Use the formula for the sum to n terms of an AP.	The sum to n terms is
	$\frac{1}{2} \times n\{2 \times 3 + 2(n-1)\}$
	$= \frac{1}{2}n\{6 + 2(n-1)\}$
	$= \frac{1}{2}n(6 + 2n - 2) = n^2 + 2n.$

You can often check answers to questions by putting specific values into general formulae. For example, putting $n = 20$ into the formula for the sum of n terms gives $20^2 + 2 \times 20 = 440$, which agrees with an earlier answer.

2 An AP is $2, 5, 8, \ldots$. Find which term of the sequence is equal to 158.

Find the values of a and d.	By inspection $a = 2$ and $d = 5 - 2 = 3$.
	Let 158 be the nth term.
Set up an equation to find which term is equal to 158.	$158 = 2 + 3(n-1)$. This leads to $n = 53$.

3 Find the sum of the second 100 terms of the arithmetic progression which begins $5, 2, -1, -4, \ldots$.

Find the values of a and d.	By inspection $a = 5$ and $d = -3$.
Find the sum of the second hundred terms by finding the sum of 200 terms and then subtracting the sum of 100 terms.	$S_{200} = \frac{1}{2} \times 200\{2 \times 5 + (-3) \times 199\}$ $= -58\,700.$ $S_{100} = \frac{1}{2} \times 100\{2 \times 5 + (-3) \times 99\}$ $= -14\,350.$

The required sum is
$$S_{200} - S_{100} = -58\,700 - (-14\,350)$$
$$= -44\,350.$$

4   The tenth term of an AP is 29 and the 20th term is 59. Find the sum of the first 30 terms.

Write the original information using a and d for the AP.	The 10th term is 29 gives the equation $a + 9d = 29$. The 20th term is 59 gives the equation $a + 19d = 59$.
Solve the two simultaneous equations to find a and d.	$\left.\begin{array}{l} a + 9d = 29 \\ a + 19d = 59 \end{array}\right\}$ gives $d = 3$, $a = 2$.
Use the values of a and d to find S_{30} by using the formula for the sum of n terms.	$S_{30} = \tfrac{1}{2} \times 30\{2 \times 2 + 3 \times 29\} = 1365.$

5   The tenth term of an AP is 579 and the 20th term is 434. Which is the first negative term?.

Write the original information using a and d for the AP.	The 10th term is 579 gives the equation $a + 9d = 579$. The 20th term is 434 gives the equation $a + 19d = 434$.
Solve the two simultaneous equations to find a and d.	The solution of these equations is $d = -14.5$ and $a = 709.5$.

Let the first negative term be the nth term.	If the nth term is negative $709.5+(n-1)\times(-14.5)<0$.
Solve this inequality.	$709.5-14.5n+14.5<0$ $724<14.5n$ or $n>49.9$.
Present the answer.	The 50th term is the first negative term.

6   The nth term of a sequence is given by the formula $4n-3$. Prove that the sequence is an arithmetic progression, and find the common difference.

To show that a sequence is an AP, you have to show that the difference between successive terms is constant throughout the sequence. Find the difference between the nth term and the $(n-1)$ th terms.

Find an expression for the $(n-1)$th term by substituting $(n-1)$ for n in the formula for the nth term.	The $(n-1)$th term is $4(n-1)-3=4n-7$.
Now find the difference between the nth and $(n-1)$th terms.	The nth term – the $(n-1)$th term is $4n-3-(4n-7)=4n-3-4n+7=4$ so the common difference is 4.
	Since the difference between the nth term and the $(n-1)$th term is a constant, and independent of n, the sequence is an AP. The common difference is 4.

7   The sum to n terms of a sequence is given by the formula $S_n=n^2-3n+1$. Find a formula for the nth term, and prove that the sequence is an arithmetic progression.

To find a formula for the nth term of a sequence, find the sum to n terms minus the sum of $(n-1)$ terms.

Find an expression for the sum to $(n-1)$ terms by substituting $(n-1)$ for n in the formula for S_n.

The sum to $(n-1)$ terms is
$$S_{n-1} = (n-1)^2 - 3(n-1) + 1$$
$$= n^2 - 2n + 1 - 3n + 3 + 1.$$
$$= n^2 - 5n + 5.$$

Now find the difference between S_n and S_{n-1} to find the nth term.

The nth term $= S_n - S_{n-1}$
$$= n^2 - 3n + 1 - \left(n^2 - 5n + 5\right)$$
$$= 2n - 4.$$

Use the method of Example 5 to find the difference between the nth and the $(n-1)$th terms.

The nth term $-$ the $(n-1)$th term is
$$2n - 4 - \{2(n-1) - 4\}$$
$$= 2n - 4 - \{2n - 2 - 4\}$$
$$= 2n - 4 - 2n + 6 = 2.$$
so the common difference is 2.

Since the difference between the nth term and the $(n-1)$th term is a constant, and independent of n, the sequence is an AP whose common difference is 2.

8   The fifth term of an AP with 80 terms is 16, and the eighth term is 25. Find the last term and the sum of the AP.

Find a and d from the information about the fifth and eighth terms.

$a + 4d = 16$ and $a + 7d = 25$.
Subtracting gives $3d = 9$ so $d = 3$.
Substituting $d = 3$ gives $a = 4$.

Help yourself to advanced algebra

Use the formula $l = a + (n-1)d$ to find the last term.	The last term is the 80th term, so $l = 4 + (80-1) \times 3 = 241$.
Use the formula $S_n = \frac{1}{2}n(a+l)$ to find the sum.	From $S_n = \frac{1}{2}n(a+l)$, $S_{80} = \frac{1}{2} \times 80 \times (4 + 241) = 9800$.

Exercise 8

In questions 1 to 4, if the given progression is an AP, identify the first term and give the common difference.

1   $1, 2, 3, \ldots$ 2 $1, \frac{1}{2}, \frac{1}{3}, \ldots$

3   $a, 2a, 3a, \ldots$ 4 $2, -1\frac{1}{2}, -5, \ldots$

In questions 5 to 8 write down the 15th, 25th and nth terms of the given arithmetic progressions.

5   $1, 3, 5, \ldots$ 6 $5, 3, 1, \ldots$

7   $-100, -96, -92, \ldots$ 8 $2, -1\frac{1}{2}, -5, \ldots$

9   Write down the 10th and the $(n+1)$th terms of the AP $5, 8, 11, \ldots$.

10   Write down the $(n-1)$th and $(2n)$th terms of the AP $1, -\frac{1}{2}, -2, \ldots$.

11   Which term of the AP $-3, 4, 11, \ldots$ is 998?

12   Which term of the AP $100, 97, 94, \ldots$ is -200?

13   Find the first term in the AP $241, 237, 233, \ldots$ which is negative.

14   Which term of the AP $1, 4, 7, \ldots$ is equal to $6n - 2$?

15   The fifth term of an AP is 7 and the 9th term is 43. Find the first term and the common difference.

16   The seventh term of an AP is -14, and the sum of seven terms is -35. Find the first term and the common difference.

17   The sum to n terms of the AP $1, 4, 7, \ldots$ is 1335. Find n.

18   Find the smallest value of n such that the sum to n terms of the AP with first term 2000 and common difference -100 is negative.

19   Find the sum of the odd numbers lying between 100 and 200.

20   The sum of 20 terms of an AP is 200, and the sum of 40 terms is 400. Find the first term and the common difference.

38

2 1 An employee earns £10,000 in the first year, and the income is increased every year by £800. Find the total earned in 40 full years work.

2 2 Find a formula for the sum to n terms of the sequence $1, 3, 5, \ldots$.

2 3 The first term of an AP is 4 and the last term is 45. Given that its sum is 343, find the number of terms.

2 4 The sum of an AP with first term -14 and 26 terms is 585. Find the last term.

2 5 The last term of an AP with 24 terms is 47, and its sum is 1296. Find the first term, and the common difference.

2 6 The ninth term of an AP with 50 terms is 34, and the 15th term is 22. Find the last term and the sum of the AP.

9 Geometric progressions

You will need to know

- that a geometric progression (GP) is a sequence of the form $a, ar, ar^2, \ldots$ where a is the first term, and each term is obtained from the previous one by multiplying by the common ratio r

- the formula ar^{n-1} for the nth term of the GP

- that the sum S_n of the first n terms of a GP is $S_n = \dfrac{a(r^n - 1)}{r - 1}$ or $S_n = \dfrac{a(1 - r^n)}{1 - r}$

- that the GP is convergent if and only if $-1 < r < 1$. If it is convergent, its sum S is given by $S = \dfrac{a}{1 - r}$.

If you are given several terms of a GP, you can find the common ratio by dividing any one of them by the previous one.

The key to solving problems about geometric progressions is to put given information into equations containing a, r and possibly n. Then solve these equations and use the results to derive any other information that you need.

1 The first term of a geometric progression is 3, and the common ratio is 2. Find the fifth term, the nth term, the sum to 20 terms and the sum to n terms.

The first term $a = 3$, and the common ratio $r = 2$. Use the formula for the nth term of a GP with $n = 5$.	The fifth term is $ar^4 = 3 \times 2^4 = 48$.
Use the formula for the nth term.	The nth term is $ar^{n-1} = 3 \times 2^{n-1}$.
Use the formula $S_n = \dfrac{a(r^n - 1)}{r - 1}$ for the sum on a GP, with $a = 3$, $r = 2$ and $n = 20$.	The sum to 20 terms is $S_{20} = \dfrac{3(2^{20} - 1)}{2 - 1} = 3(2^{20} - 1)$ $= 3\,145\,725.$

Use the formula for the sum to n terms of a GP.

The sum to n terms is

$$S_n = \frac{3(2^n - 1)}{2 - 1} = 3(2^n - 1).$$

You can often check answers to questions by putting specific values into general formulae. For example, putting $n = 20$ into the formula for the sum of n terms gives $3(2^{20} - 1)$, which agrees with an earlier answer.

2 A GP begins with $2, 6, 18, \dots$. Find which term of the sequence is equal to 118 098.

Find the values of a and r.

By inspection $a = 2$ and $r = \dfrac{6}{2} = 3$.

Let 118 098 be the nth term.

Set up an equation to find which term is equal to 118 098.

$118098 = 2 \times 3^{n-1}$.

Hence $3^{n-1} = 59049$.

Take logarithms to solve this equation. See Chapter 3, Example 6.

Therefore $(n-1)\log 3 = \log 59049$, so

$$n - 1 = \frac{\log 59049}{\log 3} = 10 \text{ and } n = 11.$$

3 Find the sum of the second 10 terms of the GP which begins $2, 1, \frac{1}{2}, \dots$.

Find the values of a and r.

By inspection $a = 2$ and $r = \frac{1}{2}$.

Find the sum of the second ten terms by finding the sum of the first 20 terms and then subtracting the sum of the first 10 terms.

$$S_{20} = \frac{2\left(1 - \left(\frac{1}{2}\right)^{20}\right)}{1 - \frac{1}{2}} = 4\left(1 - \left(\frac{1}{2}\right)^{20}\right).$$

$$S_{10} = \frac{2\left(1 - \left(\frac{1}{2}\right)^{10}\right)}{1 - \frac{1}{2}} = 4\left(1 - \left(\frac{1}{2}\right)^{10}\right).$$

The required sum is

$$S_{20} - S_{10} = 4\left(1 - \left(\tfrac{1}{2}\right)^{20}\right) - 4\left(1 - \left(\tfrac{1}{2}\right)^{10}\right)$$

$$= \left(\tfrac{1}{2}\right)^{8} - \left(\tfrac{1}{2}\right)^{18} \approx 0.00390.$$

4 The 10th term of a GP is 3072 and the 19th term is $-1\,572\,864$. Find the sum of the first 30 terms.

Write the original information using a and r for the GP.

The 10th term is 3072 gives the equation $ar^9 = 3072$.

The 19th term is $-1\,572\,864$ gives the equation $ar^{18} = -1\,572\,864$.

Solve the two simultaneous equations to find a and r, by dividing the second equation by the first.

$$\left.\begin{array}{l} ar^9 = 3072 \\ ar^{18} = -1\,572\,864 \end{array}\right\}$$

Therefore $\dfrac{ar^{18}}{ar^9} = \dfrac{-1\,572\,864}{3072}$ giving $r^9 = -512$ and $r = (-512)^{\frac{1}{9}} = -2$. By substitution, $a = -6$.

Use the values of a and r to find S_{30} by using the formula for the sum of n terms.

$$S_{20} = \frac{-6\left((-2)^{30} - 1\right)}{-2 - 1} = 2\left(2^{30} - 1\right)$$

$$= 2\,147\,483\,646.$$

5 Find the sum to 10 terms and the sum to infinity of the GP $1 - \tfrac{1}{2} + \tfrac{1}{4} - \ldots$.

Use the formula $S_n = \dfrac{a(1-r^n)}{1-r}$ for the sum of a GP with $a=1$ and $d=-\frac{1}{2}$.	$S_{10} = \dfrac{1\left(1-\left(-\frac{1}{2}\right)^{10}\right)}{1-\left(-\frac{1}{2}\right)}$ $= \dfrac{1-0.000976}{1.5} = 0.666\,016.$
Use the formula $S = \dfrac{a}{1-r}$ for the sum of a GP with $a=1$ and $d=-\frac{1}{2}$.	The sum to infinity is $S = \dfrac{1}{1-\left(-\frac{1}{2}\right)}$ $= \dfrac{1}{\frac{3}{2}} = \dfrac{2}{3}.$

6   The nth term of a sequence is given by the formula 3^n. Prove that the sequence is a geometric progression, and find the common ratio.

To show that a sequence is a GP, you have to show that the ratio between successive terms is constant throughout the sequence. Find the ratio between the nth term and the $(n-1)$th terms.

Find an expression for the $(n-1)$th term by substituting $(n-1)$ for n in the formula for the nth term.	The $(n-1)$th term is 3^{n-1}.
Now find the ratio of the nth term to the $(n-1)$th term.	The nth term ÷ the $(n-1)$th term is $\dfrac{3^n}{3^{n-1}} = 3$ so the common ratio is 3.
	Since the ratio between the nth term and the $(n-1)$th term is a constant, and independent of n, the sequence is a GP. The common ratio is 3.

7   The sum to n terms of a sequence is given by the formula $S_n = \frac{3}{2}(3^n-1)$. Find a formula for the nth term, and prove that the sequence is a geometric progression.

To find a formula for the nth term of a sequence, find the sum to n terms minus the sum of $(n-1)$ terms.

Find an expression for the sum to $(n-1)$ terms by substituting $(n-1)$ for n in the formula for S_n.	The sum to $(n-1)$ terms is $S_{n-1} = \frac{3}{2}\left(3^{n-1} - 1\right)$.

Now find the difference between S_n and S_{n-1} to find the nth term.

The nth term $= S_n - S_{n-1}$
$$= \frac{3}{2}\left(3^n - 1\right) - \frac{3}{2}\left(3^{n-1} - 1\right)$$
$$= \frac{3}{2}\left(3^n - 3^{n-1}\right)$$
$$= \frac{3}{2} \times 3^{n-1} \times (3-1) = 3^n.$$

Use the method of Example 6 to find the ratio of the nth term to the $(n-1)$th term.

The nth term $\div$ the $(n-1)$th term is
$$\frac{3^n}{3^{n-1}} = 3$$
so the common ratio is 3.

Since the ratio between the nth term and the $(n-1)$th term is a constant, and independent of n, the sequence is a GP whose common ratio is 3.

8 Show that the infinite recurring decimal $d = 0.81\,81\,81\ldots$ can be written as a GP, and find its sum as a fraction.

Separate out the recurring part, and write it in fractional form.

$$d = \frac{81}{100} + \frac{81}{10\,000} + \frac{81}{1\,000\,000} + \ldots$$

This is recognisable as a GP.

This is a GP with first term $\frac{81}{100}$ and common ratio $\frac{1}{100}$.

Use the formula $\dfrac{a}{1-r}$ to find d.

Using $\dfrac{a}{1-r}$, $d = \dfrac{\frac{81}{100}}{1-\frac{1}{100}} = \dfrac{81}{99} = \dfrac{9}{11}$.

9 Find the sum S of the infinite GP $1, \frac{1}{2}, \frac{1}{4}, \ldots$, and find after how many terms the sum S_n is within 10^{-6} of S.

Use the formula $S = \dfrac{a}{1-r}$ for the sum of an infinite GP to find S.

For this GP, $a = 1$, $r = \frac{1}{2}$, so
$$S = \dfrac{1}{1-\frac{1}{2}} = 2.$$

Find the sum S_n to n terms in order to find an expression for $S - S_n$.

$$S_n = \dfrac{1\left(1-\left(\frac{1}{2}\right)^n\right)}{1-\frac{1}{2}} = 2 - 2 \times \left(\tfrac{1}{2}\right)^n,$$

so $S - S_n = 2 \times \left(\tfrac{1}{2}\right)^n$.

Finding n such that $2 \times \left(\frac{1}{2}\right)^n < 10^{-6}$, or $\left(\frac{1}{2}\right)^n < 0.5 \times 10^{-6}$ is solved by taking logarithms. But remember that the logarithms are of numbers less than 1 and are therefore negative, forcing a sign change in the inequality.

Take logarithms to find n. It does not matter what the base is.

$n \log \frac{1}{2} < \log\left(0.5 \times 10^{-6}\right)$ so

As $\log \frac{1}{2}$ is negative, dividing by it reverses the sign of the inequality.

$$n > \dfrac{\log\left(0.5 \times 10^{-6}\right)}{\log \frac{1}{2}} = 20.9.$$

For 21 terms and after the sum is within 10^{-6} of the sum to infinity.

Exercise 9

In questions 1 to 6, if the given progression is a GP, identify the first term and give the common difference.

1 $1, 2, 4, 8, \ldots$ **2** $2, 4, 6, 8, \ldots$

3 $a, 2a^2, 4a^3, 8a^4, \ldots$ **4** $8, -4, 2, -1, \ldots$

5 $1, 1, 1, 1, \ldots$ **6** $a, -a, a, -a, \ldots$

In questions 7 to 10 write down the 6th, 10th and nth terms of the given geometric progression.

7 $\frac{1}{2}, 2, 8, 32, \ldots$ **8** $10, 100, 1000, 10000, \ldots$

9 $6, -3, 1\frac{1}{2}, -\frac{3}{4}, \ldots$ **10** $a, -a^2, a^3, -a^4, \ldots$

11   Write down the $(n+1)$th term of the GP $5, 8, \ldots$.

12   Write down the $(n-1)$th and $(2n)$th terms of the GP $1, -\frac{1}{2}, \frac{1}{4}, \ldots$.

13   Which term of the GP $3, 6, 12, \ldots$ is 3072?

14   Which term of the GP $100, -50, 25, \ldots$ is $0.024\,414\,062\,5$?

15   Find the first term in the GP $2, 6, 18, \ldots$ which is greater than a million.

16   Which term of the GP $\frac{1}{2}, 2, 8, \ldots$ is equal to 2^{4n-1}?

17   The fifth term of a GP is 16 and the 9th term is 64. Find the two possible values of the common ratio, and give the first term in each case.

18   The third term of a GP is 18, and the sum of the first three terms is 14. Find the possible values of the first term and the common ratio.

19   The sum to n terms of the GP $2, 1, \frac{1}{2}, \ldots$ is $3.999\,996\,185$. Find n.

20   Find the smallest value of n such that the sum to n terms of the GP with first term 2 and common ratio 3 is greater than 10^9.

21   Find the sum of the infinite GP $2, 1, \frac{1}{2}, \ldots$.

22   The sum of the infinite GP, $3, 3r, 3r^2, \ldots$ is 9. Find r.

23   Express the recurring decimal $0.126\,126\,126\ldots$ as a fraction.

24   An employee earns £20 000 in year 1 and receives an increase of 5% every year. Calculate how much the employee earns over a 40 year working life.

25   Three numbers 2, x and y are in geometric progression. Find y in terms of x.

26   Find the sum of the infinite GP $2, \frac{1}{2}, \frac{1}{8}, \ldots$.

27   Find after how many terms the GP $2, \frac{1}{2}, \frac{1}{8}, \ldots$ is within 10^{-9} of its sum to infinity.

10 The use of Σ notation

You will need to know

- that when you see the sign Σ you should expect to add a number of terms

- what Σ notation means in detail. This is explained below.

- that $\displaystyle\sum_{1}^{n} r = \tfrac{1}{2}n(n+1)$

- that $\displaystyle\sum_{1}^{n} r^2 = \tfrac{1}{6}n(n+1)(2n+1)$

- that $\displaystyle\sum_{1}^{n} r^3 = \tfrac{1}{4}n^2(n+1)^2$.

When you find the sum of a number of terms such as

$$4+5+6+\ldots+23$$

you need a precise notation. As it stands, you have to make an assumption, through lack of evidence to the contrary, that the three dots means that the terms always go up in steps of one.

When you write this sum using Σ notation, it appears in the form

$$4+5+6+\ldots+23 = \sum_{r=1}^{20}(r+3).$$

There are four parts to this notation.

- The Σ tells you to carry out a sum.
- The $(r+3)$ tells you what a typical term of the sum is. If you put $r=10$, you find the 10th term, namely $(10+3)$, or 13.

- You need to know where to start the sum. The $r = 1$ part of the notation tells you where to start. Thus the first term is $(1+3) = 4$.

- You need to know where to finish the sum. The 20 part of the notation tells you where to finish. In fact, the sum is sometimes written as $r = 20$ in the form $\sum\limits_{r=1}^{r=20} (r+3)$ Thus the last term is $(20+3) = 23$.

1   Write the sum $1+2+3+4$ using Σ notation.

You need to think through the four parts of the notation. The first part, that you need the Σ to denote the sum is automatic.

What is the typical term?	The rth term is r, so the sum starts $\sum r$.
What is the first term of the sum?	The first term is 1, so $r = 1$.
What is the last term of the sum?	The last term is 4, so $r = 4$.
You can gather all the information.	$1+2+3+4 = \sum\limits_{r=1}^{4} r$.

2   Write the sum $3^3 + 5^3 + 7^3 + \ldots + 21^3$ using Σ notation.

What is the typical term? This can sometimes be quite difficult.	The rth term is the cube of an odd number so it is of the form $(2r+1)^3$.
What is the first term of the sum?	The first term is 3^3, which corresponds to $r = 1$.

What is the last term of the sum?	The last term is 21^3, which corresponds to $r = 10$.
Gather all the information.	$3^3 + 5^3 + 7^3 + \ldots + 21^3 = \sum_{r=1}^{10} (2r+1)^3$.

Example 3 shows a useful device when the terms of the sum alternate in sign.

3   Write the sum $2^2 - 3^2 + 4^2 - 5^2 + 6^2 - \ldots + 20^2$ using $\sum$ notation.

What is the typical term?	The signs alternate.

The rth term is negative if r is even, and positive if r is odd. Use the form $(-1)^{r+1}$ or $(-1)^{r-1}$, it doesn't matter which, to show this. If the signs were the other way round you would use $(-1)^r$.

So what is the typical term?	Without the alternating sign the typical term is $(r+1)^2$. Taking the sign into account gives the typical term as $(-1)^{r+1}(r+1)^2$.

It is worth checking that you have the typical term correct by checking say, the third and fourth terms. In this case they are $(-1)^{3+1}(3+1)^2 = (-1)^4 4^2 = 4^2$ and $(-1)^{4+1}(4+1)^2 = (-1)^5 5^2 = -5^2$ which are corect.

What is the first term of the sum?	The first term is 2^2, which corresponds to $r = 1$.
What is the last term of the sum?	The last term is 20^2, which corresponds to $r = 19$.

| Gather all the information. | $2^2 - 3^2 + \ldots + 20^2 = \displaystyle\sum_{r=1}^{19} (-1)^{r+1}(r+1)^2.$ |

4 Write $\displaystyle\sum_{r=3}^{5} r^2$ as an ordinary sum.

The Σ tells you to have to carry out a sum. But what is the first term?	The $r=3$ tells you that the first term is that for which $r=3$. As the typical term is r^2, the first term is $3^2 = 9$.
What is the last term?	The last term is $r=5$, namely $5^2 = 25$.
You now have all the information.	$\displaystyle\sum_{r=3}^{5} r^2 = 3^2 + 4^2 + 5^2 = 9 + 16 + 25 = 50.$

The same sum can be written in different ways. Example 5 shows the same sum as Example 3, but in different notation.

5 Write $\displaystyle\sum_{r=0}^{2} (r+3)^2$ as an ordinary sum.

| What is the first term? | The $r=0$ tells you that the first term is that for which $r=0$. As the typical term is $(r+3)^2$, the first term is $(0+3)^2 = 3^2.$ |
| What is the last term? | The last term is $r=2$, namely $(2+3)^2 = 5^2.$ |

You now have all the information.

$$\sum_{r=0}^{2}(r+3)^2 = 3^2 + 4^2 + 5^2$$

$$= 9 + 16 + 25 = 50.$$

Example 5 shows not only that you can write the same sum in different ways but that you can also use the idea of the term for which $r = 0$.

6 Calculate $\sum_{r=1}^{100} r^2$.

Use the formula

$$\sum_{1}^{n} r^2 = \tfrac{1}{6}n(n+1)(2n+1) \text{ for the}$$

sum of squares given at the beginning of the chapter.

$$\sum_{r=1}^{100} r^2 = \tfrac{1}{6} \times 100 \times (100+1) \times (200+1)$$

$$= \tfrac{1}{6} \times 100 \times 101 \times 201 = 338\,350.$$

7 Calculate $\sum_{r=1}^{20}(2r+1)$.

Write $\sum_{r=1}^{20}(2r+1) = 2\sum_{r=1}^{20} r + \sum_{r=1}^{20} 1$ and

use the formula $\sum_{r=1}^{n} r = \tfrac{1}{2}n(n+1)$

given at the beginning of the chapter. Remember also that

$$\sum_{r=1}^{20} 1 = \overbrace{1+1+\ldots+1}^{20 \text{ times}} = 20.$$

$$\sum_{r=1}^{20}(2r+1) = 2\sum_{r=1}^{20} r + \sum_{r=1}^{20} 1$$

$$= 2 \times \tfrac{1}{2} \times 20 \times (20+1) + 20$$

$$= 440.$$

You may have to add and subtract terms to calculate certain sums.

8 Calculate $\displaystyle\sum_{r=8}^{16}\{(2r+1)(2r-1)\}$.

Expand $(2r+1)(2r-1)$.	$(2r+1)(2r-1)=4r^2-1$
Rewrite the sum in component form.	$\displaystyle\sum_{r=8}^{16}\{(2r+1)(2r-1)\}=4\sum_{r=8}^{16}r^2-\sum_{r=8}^{16}1$
You can now find the sum from 8 terms to 16 terms by finding the sum of the first 16 terms and subtracting the sum of the first 7 terms.	$\displaystyle 4\sum_{r=8}^{16}r^2=4\sum_{r=1}^{16}r^2-4\sum_{r=1}^{7}r^2$ $=4\times\frac{1}{6}\times16\times17\times33-4\times\frac{1}{6}\times7\times8\times15$ $=5984-560=5424.$
	Also $\displaystyle\sum_{r=8}^{16}1=\overbrace{1+1+\dots+1}^{9\text{ times}}=9$.
Put the two results together.	$\displaystyle\sum_{r=8}^{16}\{(2r+1)(2r-1)\}=5424-9=5415.$

9 Find a formula in terms of n for $\displaystyle\sum_{r=n}^{2n}r^2$.

Use the add and subtract method.	$\displaystyle\sum_{r=n}^{2n}r^2=\sum_{r=1}^{2n}r^2-\sum_{r=1}^{n-1}r^2$.
Use the formula $\displaystyle\sum_{r=1}^{n}r^2=\tfrac{1}{6}n(n+1)(2n+1)$	$\displaystyle\sum_{r=1}^{2n}r^2=\tfrac{1}{6}(2n)(2n+1)(2(2n)+1)$ $=\tfrac{1}{3}n(2n+1)(4n+1).$ $\displaystyle\sum_{r=1}^{n-1}r^2=\tfrac{1}{6}(n-1)((n-1)+1)(2(n-1)+1)$ $=\tfrac{1}{6}(n-1)n(2n-1).$

Combine these results, noting that n divides both expressions.

$$\sum_{r=n}^{2n} r^2 = \tfrac{1}{3}n(2n+1)(4n+1)$$

$$-\tfrac{1}{6}(n-1)n(2n-1).$$

Factorise and simplify to obtain the final result.

$$= \tfrac{1}{6}n\{2(2n+1)(4n+1)-(n-1)(2n-1)\}$$

$$= \tfrac{1}{6}n\{(16n^2+12n+2)-(2n^2-3n+1)\}$$

$$= \tfrac{1}{6}n(14n^2+15n+1)$$

$$= \tfrac{1}{6}n(n+1)(14n+1).$$

Exercise 10

In questions 1 to 10, write the sums using $\sum$ notation.

1   $2+3+4+5$

2   $2^2+3^2+4^2+5^2$

3   $2^2+4^2+6^2+\ldots+20^2$

4   $4^3+6^3+8^3+\ldots+20^3$

5   $\dfrac{1}{2}+\dfrac{1}{3}+\dfrac{1}{4}+\ldots+\dfrac{1}{n}$

6   $1-\dfrac{1}{2^2}+\dfrac{1}{3^2}-\dfrac{1}{4^2}+\ldots-(-1)^2\dfrac{1}{n^2}$

7   $1-\dfrac{1}{2}+\dfrac{1}{3}-\dfrac{1}{4}+\ldots+\dfrac{1}{2n+1}$

8   $1-\dfrac{1}{\sqrt{2}}+\dfrac{1}{\sqrt{3}}-\dfrac{1}{4}+\ldots-\dfrac{1}{\sqrt{100}}$

9   $(n+1)^2+(n+2)^2+\ldots+(2n)^2$

10 $\dfrac{1}{n+1}-\dfrac{1}{n+2}+\ldots+(-1)^n\dfrac{1}{2n}$

In questions 11 to 20 write the summations as an ordinary sum.

11 $\displaystyle\sum_{r=2}^{4}(r+1)$

12 $\displaystyle\sum_{r=0}^{5}\dfrac{1}{r+1}$

13 $\displaystyle\sum_{r=3}^{5}1$

14 $\displaystyle\sum_{r=a}^{b}r$

15 $\displaystyle\sum_{r=4}^{8}\dfrac{1}{2r}$

16 $\displaystyle\sum_{r=n}^{2n}r^3$

17 $\displaystyle\sum_{r=2}^{6}(-1)^r r^2$

18 $\displaystyle\sum_{r=2}^{6}(-1)^{r+1}r^2$

19 $\displaystyle\sum_{r=n+1}^{2n+1}(2r+1)^3$

20 $\displaystyle\sum_{r=4}^{8}(-1)^n(2r+1)^3$

Use the formulae given at the beginning of the chapter to calculate the values of the following sums.

21 $\displaystyle\sum_{r=1}^{10}r$

22 $\displaystyle\sum_{r=1}^{20}r^2$

23 $\displaystyle\sum_{r=1}^{30}r^3$

24 $\displaystyle\sum_{r=1}^{10}(r+1)$

25 $\displaystyle\sum_{r=1}^{12}(2r+1)$

26 $\displaystyle\sum_{r=1}^{20}(2r)^2$

27 $\displaystyle\sum_{r=1}^{20}(r+1)^2$

28 $\displaystyle\sum_{r=1}^{40}\left(r^2+3r+2\right)$

29 $\displaystyle\sum_{r=1}^{20}(3r+7)$

30 $\displaystyle\sum_{r=1}^{20}(3r+2)^3$

31 $\displaystyle\sum_{r=10}^{30}r^3$

32 $\displaystyle\sum_{r=1}^{40}\left(r^2-4r+3\right)$

Find the following sums in terms of *n*.

33 $\displaystyle\sum_{r=n+1}^{2n}r$

34 $\displaystyle\sum_{r=1}^{2n}(2r)^2$

35 $\displaystyle\sum_{r=1}^{n}(2r-1)^2$

36 $\displaystyle\sum_{r=1}^{n}(2r-1)$

37 $\displaystyle\sum_{r=1}^{n}(r-1)^3$

38 $\displaystyle\sum_{r=n+1}^{2n}r^3$

39 $3^2+6^2+\ldots+(3n)^2$

40 $1^3+3^3+5^3+\ldots+(2n-1)^3$

11 The remainder theorem

You will need to know

- the remainder theorem, that if $P(x)$ is a polynomial in x, then the remainder when it is divided by $(x-a)$ is $P(a)$

- the remainder when $P(x)$ is divided by $(ax+b)$ is $P\left(-\dfrac{b}{a}\right)$

- the factor theorem, that if $P(a) = 0$, then the polynomial is exactly divisible by $(x-a)$.

1   Find the remainder when $2x^2 - 3x + 4$ is divided by $x - 5$.

	Let $P(x) = 2x^2 - 3x + 4$.
Use the remainder theorem by substituting $x = 5$ in $P(x)$.	The remainder when dividing by $x - 5$ is $P(5)$. $P(5) = 2 \times 5^2 - 3 \times 5 + 4$ $\qquad = 50 - 15 + 4 = 39$.
Present the answer.	The remainder on dividing $2x^2 - 3x + 4$ by $x - 5$ is 39.

2   Show that $(x - 3)$ is a factor of $x^3 - 6x^2 + 11x - 6$.

	Let $P(x) = x^3 - 6x^2 + 11x - 6$.
Use the remainder theorem by substituting $x = 3$ in $P(x)$.	$P(3) = 3^3 - 6 \times 3^2 + 11 \times 3 - 6$ $\qquad = 27 - 54 + 33 - 6 = 0$.
	As $P(3) = 0$, $(x - 3)$ is a factor of $P(x)$.

3 Show that $(x-4)$ is not a factor of $x^3 - x^2 + 3x - 8$.

	Let $P(x) = x^3 - x^2 + 3x - 8$.
Use the remainder theorem by substituting $x = 4$ in $P(x)$.	$P(4) = 4^3 - 4^2 + 3 \times 4 - 8$ $\qquad = 64 - 16 + 12 - 8 = 52$.
Since the remainder is not 0, $(x-4)$ is not a factor of $x^3 - x^2 + 3x - 8$.	As $P(4) = -52 \neq 0$, $(x-4)$ is not a factor of $P(x)$.

4 Find the remainder when $2x^3 + 3x^2 + 2x + 1$ is divided by $(2x+1)$.

	Let $P(x) = 2x^3 + 3x^2 + 2x + 1$.
Use the remainder theorem by substituting $x = -\frac{1}{2}$ in $P(x)$.	$P\left(-\frac{1}{2}\right) = 2 \times \left(-\frac{1}{2}\right)^3 + 3 \times \left(-\frac{1}{2}\right)^2$ $\qquad\qquad + 2 \times \left(-\frac{1}{2}\right) + 1$ $\qquad = -\frac{1}{4} + \frac{3}{4} - 1 + 1 = \frac{1}{2}$.
Present the answer.	The remainder on dividing $2x^3 + 3x^2 + 2x + 1$ by $(2x+1)$ is $\frac{1}{2}$.

You can sometimes find the factors of a polynomial using the remainder theorem. Here is an example.

5 Find the factors of $2x^3 - 9x^2 + 7x + 6$.

You can show that if $(ax+b)$ is a factor of this polynomial, then a divides the coefficient of the highest power of x, that is 2, and that b divides the constant term, that is -6. Therefore the only possible values for a are $a = \pm 1$ and $a = \pm 2$, and the only possible values for b are $b = \pm 1, \pm 2, \pm 3$ and ± 6.

Let $P(x) = 2x^3 - 9x^2 + 7x + 6$.

Try the possible factors one by one, with the easiest, that is $x-1$, first.

Try $x-1$ as a factor.
$P(1) = 2 \times 1^3 - 9 \times 1^2 + 7 \times 1 + 6$
$= 2 - 9 + 7 + 6 = 6$.
As $P(1) \neq 0$, $x-1$ is not a factor.

Now try $x-2$ as a factor.

Try $x-2$ as a factor.
$P(2) = 2 \times 2^3 - 9 \times 2^2 + 7 \times 2 + 6$
$= 16 - 36 + 14 + 6 = 0$.
As $P(2) = 0$, $x-2$ is a factor of $P(x)$.

You could try other possible factors now, but it is better to use long division or some other method to divide $P(x)$ by $x-2$ and then factorise the remaining quadratic factor of $P(x)$ by inspection.

Divide $P(x)$ by $x-2$, and factorise the remaining quadratic factor.

$P(x) = (x-2)(2x^2 - 5x - 3)$
$= (x-2)(2x+1)(x-3)$.

Present the answer.

$2x^3 - 9x^2 + 7x + 6$
$= (x-2)(2x+1)(x-3)$.

6 Given that $x+2$ and $2x-1$ are factors of $P(x) = 2x^3 + hx^2 + kx + 10$ where h and k are constants, find h and k, and find the remaining factor.

As $(x+2)$ is a factor, use the remainder theorem with $x = -2$ to obtain an equation involving h and k. Simplify the resulting equation by dividing both sides by 2.

Since $(x+2)$ is a factor, $P(-2) = 0$.
$P(-2) = 2 \times (-2)^3 + h \times (-2)^2$
$\qquad + k \times (-2) + 10$
$= -16 + 4h - 2k + 10$
$= 4h - 2k - 6 = 0$.
Therefore $2h - k = 3$.

Do the same with $x = \frac{1}{2}$, and then simplify the result by multiplying both sides of the resulting equation by 4.

Since $(2x-1)$ is a factor, $P\left(\frac{1}{2}\right) = 0$.

$$P\left(\tfrac{1}{2}\right) = 2 \times \left(\tfrac{1}{2}\right)^3 + h \times \left(\tfrac{1}{2}\right)^2$$
$$+ k \times \left(\tfrac{1}{2}\right) + 10$$
$$= \tfrac{1}{4} + \tfrac{1}{4}h + \tfrac{1}{2}k + 10$$
$$= \tfrac{1}{4}h + \tfrac{1}{2}k + 10\tfrac{1}{4} = 0.$$
Therefore $h + 2k = -41$.

Solve the pair of simultaneous equations.

$2h - k = 3$ and $h + 2k = -41$ give
$h = -7$ and $k = -17$.

Now find the remaining factor by inspection, by examining the term in x^3 and the constant term.

$$P(x) = 2x^3 + hx^2 + kx + 10$$
$$= 2x^3 - 7x^2 - 17x + 10$$
$$= (x+2)(2x-1)(x-5).$$

Exercise 11

In questions 1 to 22 find the remainder when the given polynomial is divided by the given expression.

1   $x^2 + 2x - 3$ by $x - 1$ 2 $x^2 + 2x - 3$ by $x + 1$
3   $x^2 + 2x - 3$ by $x - 2$ 4 $2x^2 - 3x + 2$ by $x - 1$
5   $2x^2 - 3x + 2$ by $x - 2$ 6 $2x^2 - 3x + 2$ by $x + 2$
7   $2x^2 - x - 3$ by $x + 1$ 8 $2x^2 - x - 3$ by $x - 3$
9   $2x^2 - x - 3$ by $x + 3$ 10 $3x^3 - 2x^2 - 5x + 3$ by $x - 1$
11   $3x^3 - 2x^2 - 5x + 3$ by $x + 1$ 12 $3x^3 - 2x^2 - 5x + 3$ by $x - 2$
13   $2x^3 - 5x^2 - x + 6$ by $x + 1$ 14 $2x^3 - 5x^2 - x + 6$ by $x - 2$
15   $2x^3 - 5x^2 - x + 6$ by $x - 3$ 16 $4x^3 - 2x^2 + 5x - 3$ by $2x - 1$
17   $4x^3 - 2x^2 + 5x - 3$ by $2x - 3$ 18 $4x^3 - 2x^2 + 5x - 3$ by $2x + 3$
19   $6x^3 + 3x^2 - 7x - 2$ by $2x - 3$ 20 $6x^3 + 3x^2 - 7x - 2$ by $3x + 1$
21   $6x^3 + 3x^2 - 7x - 2$ by $3x + 2$ 22 $6x^3 + 3x^2 - 7x - 2$ by x

In questions 23 to 34 factorise the given expressions.

23   $x^3 + 4x^2 + x - 6$ 24 $a^3 - 3a - 2$
25   $d^3 - 3d^2 - 10d + 24$ 26 $m^3 + 4m^2 - 9m - 36$

27 $c^3 - 4c^2 - 3c + 18$ **28** $u^3 + 3u^2 + 3u + 2$

29 $n^3 - n^2 - 3n - 9$ **30** $2y^3 + 3y^2 - 8y + 3$

31 $2x^3 + x^2 - 15x - 18$ **32** $m^3 - 5m^2 - 22m + 56$

33 $n^3 - 3n + 2$ **34** $a^3 + 3a^2 - 4a - 12$

35 $b^3 - 19b - 30$ **36** $6z^3 - 17z^2 + 4z + 12$

37 Given that $x - 3$ is a factor of $2x^3 + ax^2 - 5x + 6$, find a and the remaining factor of the expression.

38 When the polynomial $x^4 - 5x^2 + bx - 4$ is divided by $x + 2$ the remainder is -4. Find b and the remainder when the polynomial is divided by $x - 3$.

39 Given that $x + 3$ is a factor of $x^3 + cx + 6$, find the other two factors.

40 Given that $x^4 + x^3 + ax^2 + bx - 2b$ is exactly divisible by $x + 2$ and $x - 3$, find a and b and the other two factors.

41 If $ax^3 + bx^2 + x - a$ is exactly divisible by $x + 3$ and by $2x - 1$, find a and b and the other factor.

42 If $ax^4 + bx^3 + 7x + 2b$ is divided by $x - 1$ the remainder is -2, and if divided by $x + 2$ the remainder is 58. Find a and b.

43 An expression of the form $ax^2 + bx + c$ is exactly divisible by $x - 3$, and the remainders when it is divided by $x - 1$ and $x + 1$ are respectively -6 and 4. Find the expression.

44 The factors of $ax^3 + bx^2 + cx + 2$ are $x - 1$, $x + 2$ and $2x - 1$. Find a, b and c.

45 Two factors of $ax^3 + bx^2 + cx - 2$ are $x + 1$ and $2x + 1$. The remainder when the expression is divided by $x + 2$ is -12. What is the third factor in the expression?

46 A factor of $ax^3 + bx + a + b$ is $x + 4$. When the expression is divided by $x + 2$ the remainder is 14. Find the other two factors of the expression.

12 Equating coefficients

You will need to know

● how to multiply out brackets

● the meaning of the terms, quotient, remainder, divisor.

1   $2x+3$ divides into $8x^2 + 2x - 15$. Find the other factor.

You might be able to see the answer by inspection.

Write out the calculation using letters for the unknown coefficients.	Let $8x^2 + 2x - 15 = (2x+3)(Ax+B)$ where A and B are constants.
Multiply out the brackets.	$8x^2 + 2x - 15$ $= 2Ax^2 + x(3A+2B) + 3B.$
Now equate the coefficients of the various powers of x.	Equating coefficients: x^2 terms : $\qquad 8 = 2A$ x terms : $\qquad 2 = 3A + 2B$ Constant term: $\quad -15 = 3B$
Solve these equations.	Therefore $A = 4$, $B = -5$.
Present the answer.	$8x^2 + 2x - 15 = (2x+3)(4x-5).$

2   $(x+2)$ divides into $4x^2 - 3x + 6$. Find the quotient and the remainder.

You could divide $4x^2 - 3x + 6$ directly by $(x+2)$. Here is another technique which uses the idea of equating coefficients.

Write out the calculation using letters for the unknown coefficients.	Let $4x^2 - 3x + 6 = (x+2)(Ax+B) + C$ where A, B and C are constants.

Multiply out the brackets.	$4x^2 - 3x + 6$
	$= Ax^2 + x(2A + B) + 2B + C.$

Now equate the coefficients of the various powers of x.	Equating coefficients:
	x^2 terms : $\quad 4 = A$
	x terms : $\quad -3 = 2A + B$
	Constant term: $\quad 6 = 2B + C$

Solve these equations.	Therefore $A = 4$, $B = -11$, $C = 28$.

Present the answer.	$4x^2 - 3x + 6 = (x + 2)(4x - 11) + 28.$

3 One factor of $8x^3 - 14x^2 - 19x + 30$ is $2x + 3$. Factorise $8x^3 - 14x^2 - 19x + 30$ completely.

Write out the calculation using letters for the unknown coefficients.	Let $8x^3 - 14x^2 - 19x + 30$
	$= (2x + 3)(Ax^2 + Bx + C)$
	where A, B and C are constants.

Multiply out the brackets.	$8x^3 - 14x^2 - 19x + 30$
	$= 2Ax^3 + x^2(3A + 2B)$
	$+ x(3B + 2C) + 3C.$

Now equate the coefficients of the various powers of x.	Equating coefficients:
	x^3 terms : $\quad 8 = 2A$
	x^2 terms : $\quad -14 = 3A + 2B$
	x terms : $\quad -19 = 3B + 2C$
	Constant term: $\quad 30 = 3C$

Solve these equations.	From the first three equations: $A = 4, B = -13, C = 10$.

Note that the value of C checks with the last equation.

Now factorise completely.	$8x^3 - 14x^2 - 19x + 30$ $= (2x+3)(4x^2 - 13x + 10)$ $= (2x+3)(x-2)(4x-5)$.

4 $\quad \dfrac{3x^3 + 4x^2 + 5x - 7}{3x - 2} = Ax^2 + Bx + C + \dfrac{D}{3x - 2}$ where A, B, C and D are constants.

Find A, B, C and D.

Multiply both sides by $3x - 2$.	$3x^3 + 4x^2 + 5x - 7$ $= Ax^2(3x-2) + Bx(3x-2)$ $\qquad + C(3x-2) + D.$

Sort out the powers of x on the right-hand side.	$3x^3 + 4x^2 + 5x - 7$ $= 3Ax^3 + x^2(-2A + 3B)$ $\qquad + x(-2B + 3C) - 2C + D.$

Now equate the coefficients of the various powers of x.	Equating coefficients: x^3 terms : $\qquad 3 = 3A$ x^2 terms : $\qquad 4 = -2A + 3B$ x terms : $\qquad 5 = -2B + 3C$ Constant term: $\quad -7 = -2C + D$

Solve these equations.	$A = 1, B = 2, C = 3, D = -1$.

When you divide one algebraic expression by another you get a quotient and a remainder. You can tell what degree the quotient is by looking at the first term of the division. And when you write the remainder it must be of power just one less than the power of the divisor. Example 5 shows the method.

5   Use the method of equating coefficients to divide $4x^4 + 8x^3 - 7x^2 - 5x + 6$ by $2x^2 + 3x - 4$.

When you express the division as a fraction, the numerator has degree 4 and the denominator has degree 2. The quotient therefore has degree 2, and is of the form $Ax^2 + Bx + C$. The remainder must have degree less than that of the divisor $2x^2 + 3x - 4$, and is therefore linear. The calculation takes the form

$$\frac{4x^4 + 8x^3 - 7x^2 - 5x + 6}{2x^2 + 3x - 4} = Ax^2 + Bx + C + \frac{Dx + E}{2x^2 + 3x - 4}.$$

You can now equate coefficients in the usual way to find A, B, C, D and E.

Multiply both sides by $2x^2 + 3x - 4$.	$4x^4 + 8x^3 - 7x^2 - 5x + 6$ $$= \left(Ax^2 + Bx + C\right)\left(2x^2 + 3x - 4\right)$$ $$+ Dx + E.$$
Sort out the powers of x on the right-hand side.	$4x^4 + 8x^3 - 7x^2 - 5x + 6$ $$= 2Ax^4 + x^3(3A + 2B)$$ $$+ x^2(-4A + 3B + 2C)$$ $$+ x(-4B + 3C + D) - 4C + E.$$
Now equate the coefficients of the various powers of x.	Equating coefficients: x^4 terms : $4 = 2A$ x^3 terms : $8 = 3A + 2B$ x^2 terms : $-7 = -4A + 3B + 2C$ x terms : $-5 = -4B + 3C + D$ Constant term: $6 = -4C + E$
Solve these equations.	$A = 2, B = 1, C = -1, D = 2, E = 2$.

Present the result. | The quotient is $2x^2 + x - 1$ and the remainder is $2x + 2$.

Exercise 12

In questions 1 to 6, a quadratic expression and a factor of it is given. Use the method of equating coefficients to find the other factor.

1 $8x^2 - 26x + 15,\ 2x - 5$ **2** $12x^2 - x - 6,\ 3x + 2$

3 $2x^2 - x - 3,\ x + 1$ **4** $6x^2 - 23x - 18,\ 3x + 2$

5 $6x^2 - x - 2,\ 2x + 1$ **6** $12x^2 + 7x - 12,\ 4x - 3$

In questions 7 to 26, use the method of equating coefficients to find the quotient and remainder when the first given expression is divided by the second.

7	$a^3 - a^2 - 3a + 2$	by	$a - 2$
8	$m^3 + 2m^2 - m + 6$	by	$m + 3$
9	$2x^3 + 7x^2 - 2x - 10$	by	$2x + 3$
10	$3u^3 - 7u^2 + 11u - 7$	by	$3u - 1$
11	$2m^3 - 9m^2n + 5mn^2 + 6n^3$	by	$2m - 3n$
12	$2x^3 + 3x^2y - 4xy^2 + y^3$	by	$2x - y$
13	$2b^3 + 7b^2c - 6c^3$	by	$2b + 3c$
14	$a^3 - 7ad^2 + 6d^3$	by	$a + 3d$
15	$9x^3 - 16x - 10$	by	$3x + 2$
16	$y^2 + 15 + 6y^3$	by	$2y + 3$
17	$3a^3 - 7a^2b + 4b^3$	by	$3a^2 - ab - 2b^2$
18	$4m^3 - 7mu^2 + 3u^3$	by	$2m^2 + mu - 3u^2$
19	$9h^3 + 8k^3 - 22hk^2$	by	$3h - 4k$
20	$31m^2n - 9n^3 + 10m^3$	by	$5m + 3n$
21	$6b^2 - 1 - 11b + 9b^3$	by	$3b^2 + 4b - 1$
22	$8 - 11a^2 + 6a^3 - 9a$	by	$2a^2 - 3a - 4$
23	$m^3 - n^3$	by	$m - n$
24	$m^3 + n^3$	by	$m^2 - mn + n^2$
25	$6u^3 + 4v^3 - 23uv^2 + 7u^2v$	by	$2u^2 - v^2 + 5uv$
26	$19mn^2 - 17m^2n + 4m^3 - 5n^3$	by	$m^2 + n^2 - 3mn$

In questions 27 to 36, one factor of the cubic expression is given. Find the other two factors.

27 $2x^3 + 5x^2 - 4x - 3,\ x - 1$

28 $8y^3 + 4y^2 - 10y + 3,\ 2y - 1$

29 $2z^3 - z^2 - 2z + 1,\ z - 1$

30 $6x^3 + 7x^2 - 1,\ x + 1$

31 $12y^3 + 40y^2 + 13y - 30,\ 2y + 3$

32 $6z^3 - 17z^2 + 6z + 8,\ z - 2$

33 $18x^3 - 9x^2 - 38x + 24,\ 3x - 2$

34 $6y^3 - 43y^2 + 91y - 60,\ y - 4$

35 $x^3 - 6x^2 y + 11xy^2 - 6y^3,\ x - y$

36 $3y^3 - 13y^2 x + 8yx^2 + 12x^3,\ y - 2x$

In questions 37 to 48, find the values of the constants A, B, C and D.

37 $\dfrac{x^3 - 3x^2 + 2x - 4}{x - 1} = Ax^2 + Bx + C + \dfrac{D}{x - 1}$

38 $\dfrac{x^3 + 4x^2 + 3x - 6}{x + 2} = Ax^2 + Bx + C + \dfrac{D}{x + 2}$

39 $\dfrac{2x^3 - 3x^2 - x + 6}{x - 3} = Ax^2 + Bx + C + \dfrac{D}{x - 3}$

40 $\dfrac{2x^3 - x^2 + x + 3}{2x + 1} = Ax^2 + Bx + C + \dfrac{D}{2x + 1}$

41 $\dfrac{4y^3 + 2y^2 - 2y + 3}{2y + 3} = Ay^2 + By + C + \dfrac{D}{2y + 3}$

42 $\dfrac{5z^3 - z^2 + 2z - 4}{2z - 1} = Az^2 + Bz + C + \dfrac{D}{2z - 1}$

43 $\dfrac{5x^3 - x^2 y + 2xy^2 - 4y^3}{x - y} = Ax^2 + Bxy + Cy^2 + \dfrac{Dy^3}{x - y}$

44 $\dfrac{2x^3 + 3x^2 y - 4xy^2 + 5y^3}{2x + 3y} = Ax^2 + Bxy + Cy^2 + \dfrac{Dy^3}{2x + 3y}$

45 $\dfrac{4m^3 - 4m^2 n + 5mn^2 - 7n^3}{2m - 5n} = Am^2 + Bmn + Cn^2 + \dfrac{Dn^3}{2m - 5n}$

46 $\dfrac{3p^3 - 7p^2 q + 6pq^2 + 32q^3}{3p + 2q} = Ap^2 + Bpq + Cq^2 + \dfrac{Dq^3}{3p + 2q}$

47 $\dfrac{6a^3 - 7a^2 b + 12ab^2 - 12b^3}{2a - b} = Aa^2 + Bab + Cb^2 + \dfrac{Db^3}{2a - b}$

48 $\dfrac{-10c^3 - 29c^2 d + 17cd^2 - 2d^3}{2c + 7d} = Ac^2 + Bcd + Cd^2 + \dfrac{Dd^3}{2c + 7d}$

13 Transformations and graphs

You will need to know

- the graph of $y - c = f(x)$ or $y = f(x) + c$ is a copy of the graph of $y = f(x)$ with every point (x, y) on $y = f(x)$ translated by a distance of c in the y-direction to become $(x, y + c)$, that is, a translation of $\begin{pmatrix} 0 \\ c \end{pmatrix}$

- the graph of $y = f(x - c)$ is a copy of the graph of $y = f(x)$ with every point (x, y) on $y = f(x)$ translated by a distance of c in the x-direction to become $(x + c, y)$, that is, a translation of $\begin{pmatrix} c \\ 0 \end{pmatrix}$

- for $c > 0$, the graph of $\dfrac{y}{c} = f(x)$ or $y = cf(x)$ is a copy of the graph of $y = f(x)$ enlarged in the y-direction with every point (x, y) on $y = f(x)$ becoming the point (x, cy)

- for $c > 0$, the graph of $y = f\left(\dfrac{x}{c}\right)$ is a copy of the graph of $y = f(x)$ enlarged in the x-direction with every point (x, y) on $y = f(x)$ becoming the point (cx, y)

- the graph of $y = -f(x)$ is a reflection of the graph of $y = f(x)$ in the x-axis with every point (x, y) on $y = f(x)$ becoming the point $(x, -y)$

- the graph of $y = f(-x)$ is a reflection of the graph of $y = f(x)$ in the y-axis with every point (x, y) on $y = f(x)$ becoming the point $(-x, y)$.

1 What transformation makes the graph of $y = 3x$ into $y = 3x + 1$?

Define a function. | Let $f(x) = 3x$, so $y = 3x$ becomes $y = f(x)$.

| Now consider $y = 3x + 1$ in function notation. | The equation $y = 3x + 1$ is the same as $y = f(x) + 1$. The graph is therefore translated by a distance 1 in the positive y-direction. |

2 What transformation makes the graph of $y = x^2$ into $y = (x - 2)^2$?

| Define a function. | Let $f(x) = x^2$, so $y = x^2$ becomes $y = f(x)$. |
| Now consider $y = (x - 2)^2$ in function notation. | The equation $y = (x - 2)^2$ is the same as $y = f(x - 2)$. The graph is therefore translated by a distance 2 in the positive x-direction. |

3 What transformation makes the graph of $y = \sin x$ into $y = 2 \sin x$?

| Define a function. | Let $f(x) = \sin x$, so $y = \sin x$ becomes $y = f(x)$. |
| Now consider $y = 2 \sin x$ in function notation. | The equation $y = 2 \sin x$ is the same as $y = 2f(x)$. The graph is therefore enlarged by a factor 2 in the y-direction. |

4 What transformation makes the graph of $y = \sin x$ into $y = \sin 2x$?

| Define a function. | Let $f(x) = \sin x$, so $y = \sin x$ becomes $y = f(x)$. |
| Now consider $y = \sin 2x$ in function notation. | The equation $y = \sin 2x$ is the same as $y = f(2x)$. The graph is therefore enlarged by a factor $\frac{1}{2}$ in the x-direction. |

5   A function $y = f(x)$ is defined by the graph in Fig. 13.1. For $x < -2$ and for $x > 2$, $f(x) = 0$. Draw the graphs of $y = f(x+2)$ and $y = f(2x)$.

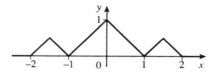

Fig. 13.1

$y = f(x+2)$ moves the graph of
$y = f(x)$ by 2 units to the left.

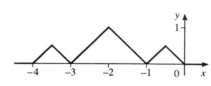

Fig. 13.2

$y = f(2x)$ stretches the graph of
$y = f(x)$ by a factor of $\frac{1}{2}$ in the
x-direction.

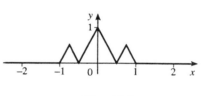

Fig. 13.3

6   The graph of $y = 2x^2$ is translated so that its vertex is at the point $(3,2)$. Find its new equation.

	The existing graph, $y = 2x^2$, has its vertex at $(0,0)$, so you need to move it to $(3,2)$.
First translate the graph by 3 units in the positive x-direction.	$y = 2x^2$ becomes $y = 2(x-3)^2$.
Next translate by 2 units in the positive y-direction.	$y = 2(x-3)^2$ becomes $y = 2(x-3)^2 + 2$.

Now simplify.

$$y = 2(x-3)^2 + 2$$
$$= 2(x^2 - 6x + 9) + 2$$
$$= 2x^2 - 12x + 20.$$

7   What transformations transform the graph of $y = \sin x$ into the graph of $y = 3\sin\left(x - \tfrac{1}{2}\pi\right)$?

First translate the graph by $\tfrac{1}{2}\pi$ units in the positive x-direction.

$y = \sin x$ becomes $y = \sin\left(x - \tfrac{1}{2}\pi\right)$.

Next enlarge by a factor of 3 in the y-direction.

$y = \sin\left(x - \tfrac{1}{2}\pi\right)$ becomes $y = 3\sin\left(x - \tfrac{1}{2}\pi\right)$.

Exercise 13

In questions 1 to 8, write down a single transformation which turns the first graph into the second. In some cases there may be more than one answer.

1   $y = 2x$ into $y = 2x + 4$
2   $y = 3x$ into $y = 3x - 6$
3   $y = x^2$ into $y = x^2 + 3$
4   $y = x^2$ into $y = (x+3)^2$
5   $y = 2^x$ into $y = 4 \times 2^x$
6   $y = x^2$ into $y = 4x^2$
7   $y = x^2$ into $y = x^2 - 4x + 4$
8   $y = \cos x$ into $y = \sin x$

In questions 9 to 16, write down new equation of the graph after the given transformation or transformations are carried out on the graph of $y = f(x)$.

9   A translation of 3 units in the y-direction.
10   A translation of -2 units in the x-direction.
11   A translation of -4 units in the y-direction.
12   A translation of 3 units in the x-direction, followed by a translation of 4 units in the y-direction.
13   A stretch of factor 4 in the y-direction.
14   A stretch of factor 4 in the y-direction, followed by a translation of -2 units in the x-direction.
15   A stretch of factor 2 in the y-direction followed by a translation of 1 unit in the y-direction.

1 6   A stretch of factor 3 in the *y*-direction followed by a stretch of factor 4 in the *x*-direction.

In questions 17 to 20, write down a pair of transformations which turn the first graph into the second.

1 7 $y = x^2$ into $y = (x+1)^2 + 2$ **1 8** $y = x^2$ into $y = 2x^2 + 1$

1 9 $y = x^2$ into $y = x^2 - 2x + 4$ **2 0** $y = \sin x$ into $y = 3\sin\left(x - \frac{1}{3}\pi\right)$

The graph of $y = f(x)$ is given in Fig. 11.4. For $x < 1$, $f(x) = 1$, and for $x > 2$, $f(x) = 0$.

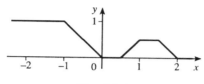

Fig. 11.4

In questions 21 to 24, draw the graph of the given function based on Fig. 11.4.

2 1 $y = f\left(\dfrac{x}{2}\right)$ **2 2** $y = f(2x) + 1$

2 3 $y = f(x-1) + 2$ **2 4** $y = 2f(2x)$

14 The language of functions

You will need to know

- that a function (or mapping) f consist of three parts:

    (i)   a starting set called the **domain**;

    (ii)   a target set called the **co-domain**;

    (iii) a rule which assigns to each element x of the domain exactly one element $f(x)$ of the co-domain

- that the element $f(x)$ of the co-domain is called the **image** of x

- that the set of images of the domain is called the **range** of the function f

- that if the range is identical with the co-domain, the function is called **onto**

- that if each element in the range of f is the image of exactly one element of the domain, the function is called **one to one**

- that if there is at least one element in the range of f which is the image of more than one element of the domain, the function is called **many to one**

- that if $f(x) = f(-x)$, f is **even**, and if $f(x) = -f(-x)$, f is **odd**.

Example 1

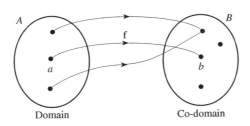

Fig. 14.1

In Fig. 14.1, the set A is the domain, the set B is the co-domain, and the rule is f. This function is sometimes written in the form $f : A \rightarrow B$. The function f is many to one because there is one element in the co-domain B which is the image of two elements in the domain A. It is not onto, because there is one element in the co-domain B which is not the image of any element in the domain A. Thus the range of f is not identical with the co-domain B.

71

Example 2

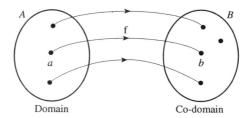

Fig. 14.2

In Fig. 14.2 the function f is one to one, because every element in the range of f is the image of exactly one element in the domain A, but it is not onto, because there is one element in the co-domain B which is not the image of any element in the domain A. Again the range of f is not identical with the co-domain B.

Example 3

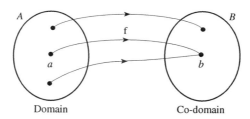

Fig. 14.3

In Fig. 14.3 the function f is onto, because every element in the co-domain B is the image of some element in the domain A. The range of f is equal to the co-domain B. However, f is not one to one, because there is one element in the co-domain B which is the image of two elements in the domain A. f is a many to one function.

Example 4

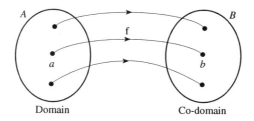

Fig. 14.4

In Fig. 14.3 the function f is both one to one and onto, because every element in the co-domain B is the image of exactly one element in the domain A. In this case, the range of f is equal to the co-domain B.

1 Let $A = \{a,b,c\}$ and $B = \{x,y\}$. Define $f : A \to B$ by $f(a) = x$, $f(b) = y$ and $f(c) = x$. Determine whether f is one to one or onto.

Note that if a statement is false, a specific reason is given.

First, is f one to one?	f is not one to one, because $f(a) = f(c)$. In fact, f is many to one.
Is f onto?	f is onto, because every element of B is the image of some element of A.

2 Define $f : \mathbf{R} \to \mathbf{R}$ by $f(x) = x^2$. Determine the range of f, and state whether f is one to one or onto, giving reasons for your answers.

The set $\mathbf{R}$ denotes the set of real numbers.

The range of f is the set of elements which are images of elements of the domain.	The range of f is the set of non-negative real numbers $y \in \mathbf{R}, y \geq 0$.
First, is f one to one?	f is not one to one, because $f(1) = f(-1) = 1$.
Is f onto?	f is not onto, because no element of the domain $\mathbf{R}$ maps to the element -1 of the co-domain.

3 Let $\mathbf{R}^+$ be the set of positive real numbers, $\mathbf{R}^+ = \{x \in \mathbf{R}, x > 0\}$. Define $f : \mathbf{R}^+ \to \mathbf{R}^+$ by $f(x) = \sqrt{x}$. Determine the range of f, and state whether f is one to one or onto, giving reasons for your answers.

The range of f is the set of elements which are images of elements of the domain.	Every element of the co-domain $\mathbf{R}^+$ has an element of $\mathbf{R}^+$ which maps to it, so the range of f is $\mathbf{R}^+$.
First, is f one to one?	f is one to one, because if $f(a) = f(b)$, $\sqrt{a} = \sqrt{b}$ so $a = b$.
Is f onto?	f is onto, because the range of f is equal to the co-domain $\mathbf{R}^+$.

In many cases it has become the custom to talk loosely about functions, and to say things such as the function $f(x) = \sin x$ or the function $f(x) = \sqrt{x}$. The assumption is that the domain is the largest subset of the real numbers $\mathbf{R}$ for which the definition makes sense, and the co-domain is the set $\mathbf{R}$.

So for the function $f(x) = \sin x$, as $\sin x$ is defined for all real numbers, the domain is $\mathbf{R}$ itself, and the range is the set $\{y \in \mathbf{R} : -1 \le y \le 1\}$, or simply $-1 \le y \le 1$.

But the function $f(x) = \sqrt{x}$ can only be defined for non-negative real numbers $\{x \in \mathbf{R} : x \ge 0\}$, and this is taken to be the domain as no domain is given. The range is the set $\{y \in \mathbf{R} : y \ge 0\}$.

4 Determine whether the functions $f(x) = \cos x$, $f(x) = e^x$ and $f(x) = x^3$ are even, odd or neither even nor odd.

You need to find out whether $f(x) = f(-x)$, $f(x) = -f(-x)$ or neither.	Let $f(x) = \cos x$. Then $f(-x) = \cos(-x)$ and since $\cos(-x) = \cos x$, $f(x) = f(-x)$. Therefore $\cos x$ is even.
	Let $f(x) = e^x$. Then $f(-x) = e^{-x}$. But since $e^{-x} \ne e^x$, and $e^{-x} \ne -e^x$, $f(x) \ne f(-x)$ and $f(x) \ne -f(-x)$. Therefore e^x is neither even nor odd.

> Let $f(x) = \sin x$. Then $f(-x) = \sin(-x)$
> and since $\sin(-x) = -\sin x$,
> $f(x) = -f(-x)$. Therefore $\sin x$ is odd.

Exercise 14

1   Let $X = \{a, b\}$ and $Y = \{x, y\}$ and define $f : X \to Y$ by $f(a) = y$ and $f(b) = x$.
    Decide whether f is one to one and onto. What is the range of f?
2   Let $X = \{a, b\}$ and $Y = \{x, y\}$ and define $f : X \to Y$ by $f(a) = y$ and $f(b) = y$.
    Decide whether f is one to one and onto. What is the range of f?
3   Find the range of $f : \mathbf{R} \to \mathbf{R}$ defined by $f(x) = \sin x$.
4   Give an example of a function $f : \mathbf{R} \to \mathbf{R}$ which is one to one, but not onto.
    Write down the range of your function.
5   Give an example of a function $f : \mathbf{R} \to \mathbf{R}$ which is onto, but not one to one.

In questions 6 to 15, the domain is $\mathbf{R}$ and the co-domain is $\mathbf{R}$. Decide which of the given rules is a suitable rule for a function, and be able to justify your answer. For those which are functions, give the range.

6   $f(x) = x^2$ 7 $f(x) = x^3$
8   $f(x) = \dfrac{1}{x}$ 9 $f(x) = \cos x$
10 $f(x) = \tan x$ 11 $f(x) = 2^x$
12 $f(x) = \sqrt{x}$ 13 $f(x) = x + 1$
14 $f(x) = \operatorname{int} x$ ($\operatorname{int} x$ is the largest integer $\le x$.)
15 $f(x)$ is the smallest real number greater than x.

16 Find the range of the function $f : \mathbf{R} \to \mathbf{R}$ defined by $f(x) = 2 - \dfrac{1}{1 + x^2}$.

The following functions are defined according to the convention outlined just before the exercises. In each case state the precise domain, and give the range.

17 $f(x) = \log_{10} x$ 18 $f(x) = \sqrt{1 - x}$
19 $f(x) = \dfrac{1}{x - 1}$ 20 $f(x) = \dfrac{1}{x^2 - 1}$

Determine whether the following functions are even or odd or neither.

21 $f(x) = \tan x$ 22 $f(x) = \ln x$
23 $f(x) = 2x + x^3$ 24 $f(x) = 2 + x^2$

15 Composition of functions: inverses

You will need to know

● the language of functions

● that if the co-domain of function f is the same as the domain of function g you can combine the two functions using composition to obtain the function gf, or g∘f

● the meaning of the identity function

● that if a function is both onto and one to one, an inverse function f^{-1} exists such that $f^{-1} \circ f = f \circ f^{-1} =$ identity

● how to calculate an inverse function, if it exists.

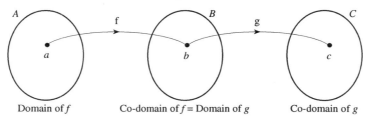

Fig. 15.1

In Fig. 15.1 $b = f(a)$ and $c = g(b)$. The composite function gf is the function which maps a from the set A directly to c in set C. It follows that $gf(a) = c$.

1 Let $f: \mathbf{R} \to \mathbf{R}$ and $g: \mathbf{R} \to \mathbf{R}$ be defined by $f(x) = 2x + 1$ and $g(x) = x^2$. Calculate $gf(2)$, $fg(2)$ and find expressions for $gf(x)$ and $fg(x)$.

Remember, gf means do f first and then g.

Find $gf(2)$. First find $f(2)$ and then g of the result. | $f(2) = 2 \times 2 + 1 = 5$ and $g(5) = 5^2 = 25$. Therefore $gf(2) = 25$.

For fg(2), first find g(2) and then f of the result.	$g(2) = 2^2 = 4$ and $f(4) = 2 \times 4 + 1 = 9$. Therefore $fg(2) = 9$.
To find $gf(x)$ you need to calculate $g(f(x)) = g(2x+1)$.	$f(x) = 2x+1$ and $gf(x) = g(f(x)) = g(2x+1) = (2x+1)^2$ $\qquad = 4x^2 + 4x + 1.$
To find $fg(x)$ you need to calculate $f(g(x)) = f(x^2)$.	$g(x) = x^2$ and $fg(x) = f(g(x)) = f(x^2) = 2x^2 + 1.$

2 Let $f : \mathbf{R} \to \mathbf{R}$ be defined by $f(x) = 3x + 2$. Find an expression for $f^{-1}(x)$.

Start by letting $y = f(x)$.	Let $y = f(x)$, so that $y = 3x + 2$.
Solve this equation for x.	$y = 3x + 2$ so $3x = y - 2$ and $x = \frac{1}{3}(y-2).$
Since $y = f(x)$, $x = f^{-1}(y)$, so $f^{-1}(y) = \frac{1}{3}(y-2)$. You must re-write this equation in terms of x.	$f^{-1}(y) = \frac{1}{3}(y-2).$ Re-writing this equation in terms of x, $f^{-1}(x) = \frac{1}{3}(x-2).$

3 Let $f : \mathbf{R} \to \mathbf{R}$ be defined by $f(x) = 1 + x^{\frac{1}{3}}$. Find an expression for $f^{-1}(x)$.

| Start by letting $y = f(x)$. | Let $y = f(x)$, so that $y = 1 + x^{\frac{1}{3}}$. |
| Solve this equation for x. | $y = 1 + x^{\frac{1}{3}}$ so $x^{\frac{1}{3}} = y - 1$ and $x = (y-1)^3.$ |

Since $y = f(x)$, $x = f^{-1}(y)$, so $f^{-1}(y) = (y-1)^3$. You must re-write this equation in terms of x.	$f^{-1}(y) = (y-1)^3$. Re-writing this equation in terms of x, $f^{-1}(x) = (x-1)^3$.

When functions are defined without being specific about the domain, such as the function $f(x) = \sqrt{x}$, you may need to take some care to ensure that the inverse function is properly defined.

4   Let $f(x) = \sqrt{x}$. Investigate whether the inverse function exists.

In order to make sense of this function, the domain has to be restricted to the set of non-negative real numbers, $x \geq 0$. The co-domain is assumed to be **R**, and, in that case no inverse is possible because the function is not onto.

However, if the co-domain of the function is restricted to be the set of non-negative real numbers, $y \geq 0$ then the function is one-to-one and onto, and an inverse exists.

In this case, you can see that the inverse function is $f^{-1}(x) = x^2$, where the domain of f^{-1} is the range of f, and the domain of f is the range of f^{-1}.

Fig. 15.2 shows the graphs of f and its inverse f^{-1}, with the restricted domains.

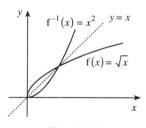

Fig. 15.2

Notice that the graphs of f and its inverse f^{-1} are reflections of each other in the line with equation $y = x$.

Restricting the domain and co-domain in this way can often enable you to define an inverse function. Here is another example.

5   Let $f(x) = \sin x$. Investigate whether the inverse function exists.

For $f(x) = \sin x$ the domain is **R**. The co-domain is assumed to be **R**, and in that case no inverse is possible because the function is not onto.

However, if the co-domain of the function is restricted to be the set $-1 \le y \le 1$ then the function is onto, but not one-to-one, so no inverse exists.

However, if you restrict the domain to $-\frac{1}{2}\pi \le x \le \frac{1}{2}\pi$, then the function is both one to one and onto, so the inverse exists.

This inverse function is $f^{-1}(x) = \sin^{-1} x$, where the domain of f^{-1}, that is $-1 \le y \le 1$, is the range of f, and and the domain of f, $-\frac{1}{2}\pi \le x \le \frac{1}{2}\pi$, is the range of f^{-1}.

Fig. 15.3 shows the graphs of f and its inverse f^{-1}, with the restricted domains.

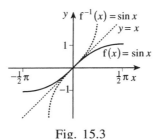

Fig. 15.3

Notice that the graphs of f and its inverse f^{-1}, shown dashed, are reflections of each other in the line with equation $y = x$.

Exercise 15

In questions 1 to 4, let $f : \mathbf{R} \to \mathbf{R}$ and $g : \mathbf{R} \to \mathbf{R}$ be two functions whose rules are given. In each case calculate the required quantities.

1 $f(x) = 2x - 3$ and $g(x) = x^2 - 1$. Find $gf(1)$ and $fg(2)$, and an expression for $gf(x)$.

2 $f(x) = \dfrac{1}{x^2 + 1}$ and $g(x) = 2x$. Find $gf(0)$ and $fg(1)$ and an expression for $fg(x)$. For what value of x is $fg(x) = f(x)$?

3 $f(x) = 4x + 3$ and $g(x) = \frac{1}{4}(x - 3)$. Find expressions for $fg(x)$ and $gf(x)$. What can you deduce about f and g?

4 $f(x) = \sin\left(\frac{1}{2}\pi x\right)$ and $g(x) = 2x$. Find expressions for $gf(x)$ and $fg(x)$. For what values of x is $fg(x) = gf(x)$?

In questions 5 to 8 find expressions for the inverses of the given functions.

5 $f : \mathbf{R} \to \mathbf{R}$ such that $f(x) = 2 - x$.

6 $f : \mathbf{R} \to \mathbf{R}$ such that $f(x) = \frac{1}{4}(2 - 3x)$.

7 $f : \mathbf{R} \to \mathbf{R}$ such that $f(x) = x^3 - 2$.

8 $f : \mathbf{R} \to \mathbf{R}$ such that $f(x) = 2x^{\frac{1}{3}} + 3$.

9 Let $A = \{x \in \mathbf{R}, x \neq 0\}$ and let B be a subset of $\mathbf{R}$ such that $f : A \to B$ given by $f(x) = \dfrac{1}{x} - 1$ has an inverse. Find B and $f^{-1}(x)$.

10 Let $A = \{x \in \mathbf{R}, x \geq 0\}$, and define $f : A \to A$ by $f(x) = \sqrt{x} + k$, where $k \geq 0$ is a constant. Show that there is just one value of k for which f has an inverse, and find an expression for the inverse function.

11 Explain why $f : \mathbf{R} \to \mathbf{R}$ defined by $f(x) = \cos x$ does not have an inverse. Show that, given suitable sets A and B, the function $g : A \to B$ such that $g(x) = \cos x$ does have an inverse. Give examples of A and B.

12 Explain why $f : \mathbf{R} \to \mathbf{R}$ defined by $f(x) = \tan x$ does not have an inverse. Show that, given suitable sets A and B, the function $g : A \to B$ such that $g(x) = \tan x$ does have an inverse. Give examples of A and B.

16 Partial fractions

You will need to know

- how to add algebraic fractions

- how to use the method of equating coefficients

- an identity, expressed by the sign $\equiv$, is true for all values of x.

1 Express $\dfrac{11-x}{(2x-1)(x+3)}$ in the form $\dfrac{A}{2x-1}+\dfrac{B}{x+3}$ where A and B are constants.

Find the values of A and B.

Write out the calculation explicitly.	Let $\dfrac{11-x}{(2x-1)(x+3)} \equiv \dfrac{A}{2x-1}+\dfrac{B}{x+3}$.
Multiply both sides by the common denominator, $(2x-1)(x+3)$.	$11-x \equiv A(x+3)+B(2x-1)$.
Equate coefficients of powers of x.	Equating coefficients: x terms: $\qquad A+2B=-1$ Constant term: $\quad 3A-B=11$
Solve these equations.	$A=3,\ B=-2$.
Present the result.	$\dfrac{11-x}{(2x-1)(x+3)} = \dfrac{3}{2x-1}-\dfrac{2}{x+3}$.

The final form in which the original algebraic fraction is split up into its fractional parts is said to be in **partial fractions**.

You must know the form in which to expect the final partial fraction result. Here is an example which goes straight to the partial fraction form.

2   Express $\dfrac{x+3}{(x+1)(x+2)}$ in partial fractions.

You must know the form in which to expect the final result. In this case you want a result in the form $\dfrac{A}{x+1} + \dfrac{B}{x+2}$ *where A and B are constants.*

Write out the calculation using letters for the unknown coefficients.	Let $\dfrac{x+3}{(x+1)(x+2)} \equiv \dfrac{A}{x+1} + \dfrac{B}{x+2}$ where A and B are constants.
Multiply both sides by the common denominator, $(x+1)(x+2)$.	$x+3 \equiv A(x+2) + B(x+1)$.
Equate coefficients of powers of x.	Equating coefficients: x terms : $\qquad A + B = 1$ Constant term: $\quad 2A + B = 3$
Solve these equations.	$A = 2,\ B = -1$.
Present the result.	$\dfrac{x+3}{(x+1)(x+2)} = \dfrac{2}{x+1} - \dfrac{1}{x+2}$.

When there are three linear factors in the denominator, the principle is the same, and extends in the way that you would expect.

3   Express $\dfrac{x^2 + 7x + 32}{(x-1)(x+2)(x+4)}$ in partial fractions.

You want a result in the form $\dfrac{A}{x-1} + \dfrac{B}{x+2} + \dfrac{C}{x+4}$ *where A, B and C are constants.*

<table>
<tr><td>Write out the calculation using letters for the unknown coefficients.</td><td>Let $\dfrac{x^2 + 7x + 32}{(x-1)(x+2)(x+4)}$

$\equiv \dfrac{A}{x-1} + \dfrac{B}{x+2} + \dfrac{C}{x+4}$
where A, B and C are constants.</td></tr>
<tr><td>Multiply both sides by the common denominator, $(x-1)(x+2)(x+4)$.</td><td>$x^2 + 7x + 32$
$\equiv A(x+2)(x+4) + B(x-1)(x+4)$
$\qquad + C(x-1)(x+2).$</td></tr>
<tr><td>Equate coefficients of powers of x.</td><td>Equating coefficients:
x^2 terms: $\qquad A + B + C = 1$
x terms: $\qquad 6A + 3B + C = 7$
Constant term: $\quad 8A - 4B - 2C = 32$</td></tr>
<tr><td>Solve these equations. See Chapter 18 for the solution of 3×3 equations.</td><td>$A = \tfrac{8}{3}, B = -\tfrac{11}{3}, C = 2.$</td></tr>
<tr><td>Present the result.</td><td>$\dfrac{x^2 + 7x + 32}{(x-1)(x+2)(x+4)}$

$= \dfrac{\frac{8}{3}}{x-1} - \dfrac{\frac{11}{3}}{x+2} + \dfrac{2}{x+4}.$</td></tr>
</table>

When there is a quadratic factor which does not factorise in the denominator, you need a different form for the partial fractions. The form has to take into account that there might be an x term in the numerator of the fraction with the quadratic denominator.

4 Express $\dfrac{5x^2 + 5x + 8}{(x+2)(x^2+2)}$ in partial fractions.

You want a result in the form $\dfrac{A}{x+2} + \dfrac{Bx+C}{x^2+2}$ *where A, B and C are constants.*

Write out the calculation using letters for the unknown coefficients.	Let $\dfrac{5x^2 + 5x + 8}{(x+2)(x^2+2)} \equiv \dfrac{A}{x+2} + \dfrac{Bx+C}{x^2+2}$ where A, B and C are constants.
Multiply both sides by the common denominator, $(x+2)(x^2+2)$.	$5x^2 + 5x + 8$ $= A(x^2+2)+(Bx+C)(x+2).$
Equate coefficients of powers of x.	Equating coefficients: x^2 terms : $\qquad A+B=5$ x terms : $\qquad 2B+C=5$ Constant term: $\quad 2A+2C=8$
Solve these equations. See Chapter 18 for the solution of 3×3 equations.	$A=3,\ B=2,\ C=1.$
Present the result.	$\dfrac{5x^2 + 5x + 8}{(x+2)(x^2+2)} = \dfrac{3}{x+2} + \dfrac{2x+1}{x^2+2}.$

If there is a repeated linear factor in the denominator, the partial fractions 'template' may take one of two forms. Which one you use will depend on the reason why you are putting the expression into partial fractions.

Examples 5 and 6 illustrate these two forms on the same expression.

5   Express $\dfrac{-x^2 + 14x + 24}{(x-2)(x+2)^2}$ in partial fractions (Method 1).

The first form is $\dfrac{A}{x-2} + \dfrac{Bx+C}{(x+2)^2}$ *where A, B and C are constants.*

Write out the calculation using letters for the unknown coefficients.	Let $\dfrac{-x^2 + 14x + 24}{(x-2)(x+2)^2} \equiv \dfrac{A}{x-2} + \dfrac{Bx+C}{(x+2)^2}.$

Multiply both sides by the common denominator, $(x-2)(x+2)^2$.	$-x^2+14x+24$ $$\equiv A(x+2)^2+(Bx+C)(x-2).$$
Equate coefficients of powers of x.	Equating coefficients: x^2 terms : $\quad A+B=-1$ x terms : $\quad 4A-2B+C=14$ Constant term: $\quad 4A-2C=24$
Solve these equations. See Chapter 18 for the solution of 3×3 equations.	$A=3, B=-4, C=-6$.
Present the result.	$\dfrac{-x^2+14x+24}{(x-2)(x+2)^2}=\dfrac{3}{x-2}-\dfrac{4x+6}{(x+2)^2}$.

6 Express $\dfrac{-x^2+14x+24}{(x-2)(x+2)^2}$ in partial fractions (Method 2).

The second form is $\dfrac{A}{x-2}+\dfrac{B}{(x+2)}+\dfrac{C}{(x+2)^2}$ *where A, B and C are constants. Note that the constants may not take the same values as in Method 1 above.*

Write out the calculation using letters for the unknown coefficients.	Let $\dfrac{-x^2+14x+24}{(x-2)(x+2)^2}$ $$\equiv\dfrac{A}{x-2}+\dfrac{B}{(x+2)}+\dfrac{C}{(x+2)^2}$$ where A, B and C are constants.
Multiply both sides by the common denominator, $(x-2)(x+2)^2$.	$-x^2+14x+24$ $$\equiv A(x+2)^2+B(x-2)(x+2)+C(x-2).$$

Equate coefficients of powers of x.	Equating coefficients:
	x^2 terms : $\qquad A + B = -1$
	x terms : $\qquad 4A + C = 14$
	Constant term: $\quad 4A - 4B - 2C = 24$
Solve these equations. See Chapter 18 for the solution of 3×3 equations.	$A = 3, B = -4, C = 2$.
Present the result.	$$\frac{-x^2 + 14x + 24}{(x-2)(x+2)^2}$$ $$= \frac{3}{x-2} - \frac{4}{(x+2)} + \frac{2}{(x+2)^2}.$$

Exercise 16

In questions 1 to 4 find the values of A and B such that the statement is true for all values of x.

1 $\quad \dfrac{5x+2}{(x-2)(x+2)} = \dfrac{A}{x-2} + \dfrac{B}{x+2}$

2 $\quad \dfrac{6x+10}{(x+3)(x-1)} = \dfrac{A}{(x+3)} + \dfrac{B}{(x-1)}$

3 $\quad \dfrac{7-x}{(x-4)(x-1)} = \dfrac{A}{(x-4)} + \dfrac{B}{(x-1)}$

4 $\quad \dfrac{11x+6}{(3x+4)(x-3)} = \dfrac{A}{(3x+4)} + \dfrac{B}{(x-3)}$

In questions 5 to 20, write the given expression in partial fractions.

5 $\quad \dfrac{2x}{(x+3)(3-x)}$ 　　　　　　**6** $\quad \dfrac{3x}{(x-2)(x+1)}$

7 $\quad \dfrac{2x+7}{(x-1)(x+2)}$ 　　　　　　**8** $\quad \dfrac{x+1}{(x+4)(x+3)}$

9 $\quad \dfrac{18-6x}{(x-2)(x-1)}$ 　　　　　**10** $\quad \dfrac{4x+3}{2x^2-7x+3}$

11 $\quad \dfrac{4}{9x^2-4}$ 　　　　　　　**12** $\quad \dfrac{6x}{9x^2-4}$

13 $\dfrac{x^2+2x+4}{(x-2)(x+2)(x+1)}$ **14** $\dfrac{10x+33}{(x-3)(2x+3)(2x+1)}$

15 $\dfrac{4x^2+40x+73}{(2x+7)(x+5)(2x+1)}$ **16** $\dfrac{1-9x}{(x+3)(x-4)(x+1)}$

17 $\dfrac{2x^2-x+7}{(x+1)(x^2+4)}$ **18** $\dfrac{x^2-x+21}{(x+2)(x^2+5)}$

19 $\dfrac{-x^2+8x-1}{(x^2+x+2)(x+5)}$ **20** $\dfrac{3x^2-53x-39}{(x^2+4x+5)(3x-2)}$

In questions 21 to 28 express the following in partial fractions in the form of Example 5.

21 $\dfrac{x^2+4x+6}{(x+1)^2(x-2)}$ **22** $\dfrac{4x^2+9x+19}{(x+3)^2(2x-1)}$

23 $\dfrac{3x^2-14x+12}{(x-2)^2(x-1)}$ **24** $\dfrac{4x^2+3x+1}{(x+1)^2(x-1)}$

25 $\dfrac{-5x^2-14x+1}{(x+2)^2(2x+1)}$ **26** $\dfrac{12x^2+38x-34}{(2x-1)^2(2x+3)}$

27 $\dfrac{64x^2+50x+9}{(2x-1)(4x+3)^2}$ **28** $\dfrac{34x+33}{(2x-1)(4x+3)^2}$

In questions 29 to 36 express the following in partial fractions in the form of Example 6.

29 $\dfrac{x^2+4x+6}{(x+1)^2(x-2)}$ **30** $\dfrac{4x^2+9x+19}{(x+3)^2(2x-1)}$

31 $\dfrac{3x^2-14x+12}{(x-2)^2(x-1)}$ **32** $\dfrac{4x^2+3x+1}{(x+1)^2(x-1)}$

33 $\dfrac{-5x^2-14x+1}{(x+2)^2(2x+1)}$ **34** $\dfrac{12x^2+38x-34}{(2x-1)^2(2x+3)}$

35 $\dfrac{64x^2+50x+9}{(2x-1)(4x+3)^2}$ **36** $\dfrac{34x+33}{(2x-1)(4x+3)^2}$

17 Binomial theorem and expansion

You will need to know

● the binomial theorem for a positive integral index

● the binomial expansion when the power is not a positive integer

● when the binomial expansion is valid.

1 Expand $(1+x)^3$ using the binomial theorem.

The binomial theorem states that for a positive integer n

$$(a+x)^n = a^n + \binom{n}{1}a^{n-1}x + \binom{n}{2}a^{n-2}x^2 + \ldots + \binom{n}{n-1}ax^{n-1} + x^n$$

where the coefficient $\binom{n}{r}$, *pronounced 'n choose r', is given by* $\dfrac{n!}{r!(n-r)!}$.

Use the binomial theorem.	$(1+x)^3 = 1^3 + \binom{3}{1}1^2 x + \binom{3}{2}1x^2 + x^3$
	$= 1 + \dfrac{3!}{1! \times 2!}x + \dfrac{3!}{2! \times 1!}x^2 + x^3$
	$= 1 + 3x + 3x^2 + x^3.$

It is tedious to have to work out the coefficients every time you want them. You should remember the formula $\binom{n}{r} = \dfrac{n!}{r!(n-r)!}$ so that you can go back to first principles to work the coefficients out, but if n is small, it is worth remembering the coefficients using Pascal's triangle, shown in Fig. 16.1.

```
        1       1
    1       2       1
  1     3       3     1
 1    4     6     4    1
1   5   10    10   5    1
```

Fig. 16.1

The coefficients in the expansion of $(a+x)^3$ are in the third row, and those of $(a+x)^5$ are in the fifth row. Each row is obtained from the row above it by using the rule that at the end of each row the number is a 1, and for the rest of the row, each number is the sum of the two above it.

2 Expand $(2+x)^4$ using the binomial theorem.

The coefficients 1, 4, 6, 4, 1 are taken from the fourth row of Pascal's triangle.

Use the binomial theorem.	$(2+x)^4 = 2^4 + 4 \times 2^3 x + 6 \times 2^2 x^2$
	$+ 4 \times 2x^3 + x^4$
	$= 16 + 32x + 24x^2 + 8x^3 + x^4.$

3 Expand $(2-3y)^5$ using the binomial theorem.

The coefficients 1, 5, 10, 10, 5, 1 are from the fifth row of Pascal's triangle.

Use the binomial theorem.	$(2-3y)^5$
	$= 2^5 + 5 \times 2^4 \times (-3y)$
	$+ 10 \times 2^3 \times (-3y)^2$
	$+ 10 \times 2^2 \times (-3y)^3$
	$+ 5 \times 2 \times (-3y)^4 + (-3y)^5$
	$= 32 - 240y + 720y^2$
	$- 1080y^3 + 810y^4 - 243y^5.$

4 Find the term in x^4 in the expansion of $(2+3x)^{10}$.

Use the binomial theorem.	The term in x^4 consists of
	$2^6 \times (3x)^4 \times \dfrac{10!}{6! \times 4!}.$
Simplify and present the answer.	The required coefficient is therefore 1 088 640.

When the exponent or power n is not a positive integer, the binomial expansion is used in a slightly different form.

First, it is used in the form $(1+x)^n$, with the first number being 1 not a. That is, it is like Example 1, and not like Examples 2 and 3.

Secondly, note that the coefficient $\dfrac{n!}{r!(n-r)!}$ in the binomial theorem can be written in the form $\dfrac{n(n-1)(n-2)...(n-r+1)}{1\times 2\times 3\times ...\times r}$. In this form, there is no need for n to be a positive integer, as it was when $n!$ was part of the expression.

The binomial expansion is written in the form

$$(1+x)^n = 1 + \frac{n}{1}x + \frac{n(n-1)}{1\times 2}x^2 + \frac{n(n-1)(n-2)}{1\times 2\times 3}x^3 + ...$$

where the term in x^r is

$$\frac{n(n-1)(n-2)...(n-r+1)}{1\times 2\times 3\times ...\times r}x^r.$$

This expansion is valid if $-1 < x < 1$.

5 Write down the first three terms of the expansion of $(1+x)^{-1}$.

Use the binomial expansion
$(1+x)^n = 1 + \dfrac{n}{1}x + \dfrac{n(n-1)}{1\times 2}x^2 + ...$
with $n = -1$.

$(1+x)^{-1} = 1 + \dfrac{(-1)}{1}x + \dfrac{(-1)(-2)}{1\times 2}x^2 + ...$

$= 1 - x + x^2 + ...$

Present your answer.

The first three terms are $1 - x + x^2$.

6 Write down the first three terms of the expansion of $(1-x)^{-\frac{1}{2}}$.

Use the binomial expansion	$(1-x)^{-\frac{1}{2}} = 1 + \dfrac{\left(-\frac{1}{2}\right)}{1}(-x) +$
$(1+(-x))^n = 1 + \dfrac{n}{1}(-x)$	$\dfrac{\left(-\frac{1}{2}\right)\left(-\frac{3}{2}\right)}{1 \times 2}(-x)^2 + \dots$
$+ \dfrac{n(n-1)}{1 \times 2}(-x)^2 + \dots$	$= 1 + \frac{1}{2}x + \frac{3}{8}x^2 + \dots .$
with $(-x)$ written for x and $n = -\frac{1}{2}$.	
Present your answer.	The first three terms are $1 + \frac{1}{2}x + \frac{3}{8}x^2$.

7 Write down the first three terms of the expansion of $(1+3x)^{-2}$. For what values of x is the expansion valid?

Use the binomial expansion	$(1+3x)^{-2} = 1 + \dfrac{(-2)}{1}(3x) +$
$(1+(3x))^n = 1 + \dfrac{n}{1}(3x)$	$\dfrac{(-2)(-3)}{1 \times 2}(3x)^2 + \dots$
$+ \dfrac{n(n-1)}{1 \times 2}(3x)^2 + \dots$	$= 1 - 6x + 27x^2 + \dots .$
with $(3x)$ written for x and $n = -2$.	
Use the fact that the expansion of $(1+x)^n$ is valid when $-1 < x < 1$.	The expansion of $(1+3x)^{-2}$ is valid for $-1 < 3x < 1$, i.e., when $-\frac{1}{3} < x < \frac{1}{3}$.
Present your answer.	The first three terms are $1 - 6x + 27x^2$. The expansion is valid for $-\frac{1}{3} < x < \frac{1}{3}$.

8 Write down the first three terms of the expansion of $(4+3x)^{-\frac{3}{2}}$. For what values of x is the expansion valid?

As $(4+3x)^{-\frac{3}{2}}$ stands, you cannot expand it. You need to re-write $(4+3x)^{-\frac{3}{2}}$ so that the bracket starts with 1. Take out the factor 4 which appears in the first term to get $(4+3x)^{-\frac{3}{2}} = \left\{4\left(1+\frac{3}{4}x\right)\right\}^{-\frac{3}{2}} = 4^{-\frac{3}{2}}\left(1+\frac{3}{4}x\right)^{-\frac{3}{2}} = \frac{1}{8}\left(1+\frac{3}{4}x\right)^{-\frac{3}{2}}$. If necessary, look up work on indices in Chapter 2.

Use the binomial expansion
$$\left(1+\left(\tfrac{3}{4}x\right)\right)^{n} = 1 + \frac{n}{1}\left(\tfrac{3}{4}x\right)$$
$$+ \frac{n(n-1)}{1\times 2}\left(\tfrac{3}{4}x\right)^{2} + \ldots$$
with $\left(\tfrac{3}{4}x\right)$ written for x and $n = -\tfrac{3}{2}$.

$$\left(1+\tfrac{3}{4}x\right)^{-\frac{3}{2}} = 1 + \frac{\left(-\tfrac{3}{2}\right)}{1}\left(\tfrac{3}{4}x\right)$$
$$+ \frac{\left(-\tfrac{3}{2}\right)\left(-\tfrac{5}{2}\right)}{1\times 2}\left(\tfrac{3}{4}x\right)^{2} + \ldots$$
$$= 1 - \tfrac{9}{8}x + \tfrac{135}{128}x^{2} + \ldots.$$

Use the fact that the expansion of $(1+x)^{n}$ is valid when $-1 < x < 1$.

The expansion of $\left(1+\tfrac{3}{4}x\right)^{-\frac{3}{2}}$ is valid for $-1 < \tfrac{3}{4}x < 1$, i.e., when $-\tfrac{4}{3} < x < \tfrac{4}{3}$.

Remember the factor $\tfrac{1}{8}$.

Therefore
$$(4+3x)^{-\frac{3}{2}} = \tfrac{1}{8}\left(1+\tfrac{3}{4}x\right)^{-\frac{3}{2}}$$
$$= \tfrac{1}{8}\left(1 - \tfrac{9}{8}x + \tfrac{135}{128}x^{2} + \ldots\right)$$
$$= \tfrac{1}{8} - \tfrac{9}{64}x + \tfrac{135}{1024}x^{2} + \ldots.$$

Present your answer.

The first three terms are $\tfrac{1}{8} - \tfrac{9}{64}x + \tfrac{135}{1024}x^{2}$.
The expansion is valid for $-\tfrac{4}{3} < x < \tfrac{4}{3}$.

9   Write down the first three terms of the expansion of $(8+x)^{\frac{1}{3}}$. For what values of x is the expansion valid?

Put $(8+x)^{\frac{1}{3}}$ into a form in which you can use the binomial expansion.

$$(8+x)^{\frac{1}{3}} = \left\{8\left(1+\tfrac{1}{8}x\right)\right\}^{\frac{1}{3}}$$
$$= 8^{\frac{1}{3}}\left(1+\tfrac{1}{8}x\right)^{\frac{1}{3}} = 2\left(1+\tfrac{1}{8}x\right)^{\frac{1}{3}}.$$

Use the binomial expansion
$$\left(1+\left(\tfrac{1}{8}x\right)\right)^{n} = 1 + \frac{n}{1}\left(\tfrac{1}{8}x\right)$$
$$+ \frac{n(n-1)}{1\times 2}\left(\tfrac{1}{8}x\right)^{2} + \ldots$$
with $\left(\tfrac{1}{8}x\right)$ written for x and $n = \tfrac{1}{3}$.

$$\left(1+\left(\tfrac{1}{8}x\right)\right)^{\frac{1}{3}} = 1 + \frac{\left(\tfrac{1}{3}\right)}{1}\left(\tfrac{1}{8}x\right)$$
$$+ \frac{\left(\tfrac{1}{3}\right)\left(-\tfrac{2}{3}\right)}{1\times 2}\left(\tfrac{1}{8}x\right)^{2} + \ldots$$
$$= 1 + \tfrac{1}{24}x - \tfrac{1}{576}x^{2} + \ldots$$

Use the fact that the expansion of $(1+x)^n$ is valid when $-1 < x < 1$.	The expansion of $\left(1+\left(\tfrac{1}{8}x\right)\right)^{\frac{1}{3}}$ is valid for $-1 < \tfrac{1}{8}x < 1$, i.e., when $-8 < x < 8$.
Remember the factor 2.	Therefore $$(8+x)^{\frac{1}{3}} = 2\left(1+\tfrac{1}{8}x\right)^{\frac{1}{3}}$$ $$= 2\left(1+\tfrac{1}{24}x - \tfrac{1}{576}x^2 + \dots\right)$$ $$= 2 + \tfrac{1}{12}x - \tfrac{1}{288}x^2 + \dots.$$
Present your answer.	The first three terms are $2 + \tfrac{1}{12}x - \tfrac{1}{288}x^2$. The expansion is valid for $-8 < x < 8$.

10 Find the first four terms of the expansion of $\left(1+x^2\right)(1+x)^{\frac{2}{3}}$.

The strategy will be to expand $(1+x)^{\frac{2}{3}}$, and to multiply the result by $\left(1+x^2\right)$.

Expand $(1+x)^{\frac{2}{3}}$, keeping terms as far as x^3, and simplify.	$$(1+x)^{\frac{2}{3}} = 1 + \frac{\tfrac{2}{3}}{1}x + \frac{\tfrac{2}{3}\left(-\tfrac{1}{3}\right)}{1\times 2}x^2$$ $$+ \frac{\tfrac{2}{3}\left(-\tfrac{1}{3}\right)\left(-\tfrac{4}{3}\right)}{1\times 2\times 3}x^3 + \dots$$ $$= 1 + \tfrac{2}{3}x - \tfrac{1}{9}x^2 + \tfrac{4}{81}x^3 + \dots.$$
Multiply by $\left(1+x^2\right)$, keeping only powers of x which are 3 or less.	$$\left(1+x^2\right)\left(1+\tfrac{2}{3}x - \tfrac{1}{9}x^2 + \tfrac{4}{81}x^3 + \dots\right)$$ $$= 1 + \tfrac{2}{3}x - \tfrac{1}{9}x^2 + \tfrac{4}{81}x^3 + x^2 + \tfrac{2}{3}x^3 + \dots$$ $$= 1 + \tfrac{2}{3}x + \tfrac{8}{9}x^2 + \tfrac{58}{81}x^3 + \dots.$$

1 1 Find the first three terms of the expansion of $\dfrac{x+3}{(1+2x)(1-3x)}$.

Use partial fractions and then expand the separate fractions.

Expand $\dfrac{x+3}{(1+2x)(1-3x)}$ in partial fractions using Chapter 16.	$\dfrac{x+3}{(1+2x)(1-3x)} = \dfrac{1}{1+2x} + \dfrac{2}{1-3x}.$
Write the right-hand side in terms of negative powers.	$= (1+2x)^{-1} + 2(1-3x)^{-1}.$
Use the binomial expansion to get the first three terms, and simplify.	$= 1 + \dfrac{(-1)}{1}2x + \dfrac{(-1)(-2)}{1\times 2}(2x)^2$ $\quad + 2\left(1 + \dfrac{(-1)}{1}(-3x) + \dfrac{(-1)(-2)}{1\times 2}(-3x)^2\right)$ $= 3 + 4x + 22x^2.$

Here is a second method to find the expansion of $\dfrac{x+3}{(1+2x)(1-3x)}$.

1 2 Find the first three terms of the expansion of $\dfrac{x+3}{(1+2x)(1-3x)}$.

Write $\dfrac{x+3}{(1+2x)(1-3x)}$ in the form $(x+3)(1-x-6x^2)^{-1}$.	$(x+3)(1-x-6x^2)^{-1}$ $= (x+3)\left(1+\left(-x-6x^2\right)\right)^{-1}.$
Use the binomial expansion.	$= (x+3)\left(\begin{array}{l}1 + \dfrac{(-1)}{1}\left(-x-6x^2\right) \\ + \dfrac{(-1)(-2)}{1\times 2}\left(-x-6x^2\right)^2\end{array}\right).$

Simplify the terms in the second bracket, keeping only the terms of power less than x^3. Simplify.

$= (x+3)(1+x+6x^2+x^2)$

$= 3+4x+22x^2.$

Exercise 16

In questions 1 to 16 use the binomial theorem to expand the following expressions.

1	$(1+x)^4$	**2**	$(1+y)^2$
3	$(1+2x)^3$	**4**	$(1+3x)^4$
5	$(2+3x)^2$	**6**	$(3+2x)^3$
7	$(2+y)^5$	**8**	$(1-x)^4$
9	$(1-2x)^3$	**10**	$(4-x)^3$
11	$(4+3x)^4$	**12**	$(3-2x)^3$
13	$\left(2-\tfrac{1}{2}x\right)^3$	**14**	$\left(x\sqrt{2}+y\right)^2$
15	$(x+2y)^3$	**16**	$(3x-2y)^4$

In questions 17 to 24, find the coefficient of the given power of x in the expansion.

17	$(1+x)^9,\ x^7$	**18**	$(1-x)^{11},\ x^8$
19	$(1+2x)^8,\ x^5$	**20**	$(2+x)^9,\ x^6$
21	$(2+5x)^{12},\ x^4$	**22**	$\left(2-3x^2\right)^{10},\ x^{14}$
23	$(3-4x)^8,\ x^5$	**24**	$\left(2-\sqrt{x}\right)^{10},\ x^4$

In questions 25 to 40, give the first three terms of the expansion, and the values of x for which it is valid.

25	$(1+x)^{-2}$	**26**	$(1+x)^{\frac{3}{2}}$
27	$(1+x)^{-3}$	**28**	$(1+x)^{\frac{2}{3}}$
29	$(1+x)^{-\frac{1}{2}}$	**30**	$(1+x)^{-\frac{1}{4}}$
31	$(1-x)^{-1}$	**32**	$(1-x)^{-\frac{1}{3}}$
33	$(1+2x)^{-2}$	**34**	$(1+3x)^{\frac{3}{2}}$
35	$\left(1-\tfrac{1}{2}x\right)^{-3}$	**36**	$(1-4x)^{\frac{2}{3}}$
37	$(1+3x)^{-\frac{1}{2}}$	**38**	$\left(1+\tfrac{1}{3}x\right)^{-\frac{1}{4}}$
39	$(1-2x)^{-1}$	**40**	$(1-4x)^{-\frac{1}{3}}$

In questions 41 to 48, re-write the given expression in the form $a(1+bx)^n$, giving the values of a and b.

41 $\quad (2+3x)^{-2}$

42 $\quad (3-5x)^{-1}$

43 $\quad (4+2x)^{\frac{1}{2}}$

44 $\quad (3+2x)^{-\frac{1}{2}}$

45 $\quad (8+3x)^{\frac{2}{3}}$

46 $\quad (9-2x)^{\frac{3}{2}}$

47 $\quad (3-6x)^{-2}$

48 $\quad (4-3x)^{-\frac{3}{2}}$

In questions 49 to 64, give the first three terms of the expansion, and the values of x for which it is valid.

49 $\quad (2+3x)^{-2}$

50 $\quad (3-5x)^{-1}$

51 $\quad (4+2x)^{\frac{1}{2}}$

52 $\quad (3+2x)^{-\frac{1}{2}}$

53 $\quad (8+3x)^{\frac{2}{3}}$

54 $\quad (9-2x)^{\frac{3}{2}}$

55 $\quad (1+x)(3-6x)^{-2}$

56 $\quad (1-x^2)(4-3x)^{-\frac{3}{2}}$

57 $\quad (1+2x)(1-3x)^{-\frac{1}{3}}$

58 $\quad (1+2x^2)(1-5x)^{\frac{1}{2}}$

59 $\quad \dfrac{1+x}{1-2x}$

60 $\quad \dfrac{2-x}{2+3x}$

61 $\quad \dfrac{1}{(1-x)(1+2x)}$

62 $\quad \dfrac{1+x}{(1-2x)(2+x)}$

63 $\quad \dfrac{1+2x}{\sqrt{(2-x)(2+x)}}$

64 $\quad \dfrac{1}{\sqrt{(1-x)(1+2x)^3}}$

18 3×3 simultaneous equations with a unique solution

You will need to know

● how to solve 2×2 simultaneous equations by elimination.

The method is essentially an extension of the one that you use for 2×2 simultaneous equations, with one important change which is good practice for the future. At each stage you should keep a set of equations which is equivalent to the given equations.

1 Solve the simultaneous equations
$$x + 2y - z = 6$$
$$2x - 3y + z = -5$$
$$x + y - 2z = 5$$

Subtract $2 \times$ the top equation from the middle equation to eliminate x from the middle equation.

$$\left. \begin{array}{l} x + 2y - z = 6 \\ -7y + 3z = -17 \\ x + y - 2z = 5 \end{array} \right\}$$

Subtract the top equation from the bottom equation to eliminate x from the bottom equation.

$$\left. \begin{array}{l} x + 2y - z = 6 \\ -7y + 3z = -17 \\ -y - z = -1 \end{array} \right\}$$

Multiply the bottom equation by 7 and subtract the middle equation from the bottom equation to eliminate y from the bottom equation.

$$\left. \begin{array}{l} x + 2y - z = 6 \\ -7y + 3z = -17 \\ -10z = 10 \end{array} \right\}$$

Find z from the last equation, and substitute to find y in the second equation.

$$\left. \begin{array}{l} x + 2y - z = 6 \\ y = 2 \\ z = -1 \end{array} \right\}$$

Use the values of z and y and substitute them in the first equation to find x.

$$\left. \begin{array}{l} x = 1 \\ y = 2 \\ z = -1 \end{array} \right\}$$

Notice that you can interchange equations if it is helpful. For instance, in Example 1 you may have found it easier at the second stage to interchange the second and third equations.

The solution then reads as follows.

2   Solve the simultaneous equations
$$\begin{array}{l} x + 2y - z = 6 \\ 2x - 3y + z = -5 \\ x + y - 2z = 5 \end{array}$$

Subtract $2 \times$ the top equation from the middle equation to eliminate x from the middle equation.

$$\left. \begin{array}{l} x + 2y - z = 6 \\ -7y + 3z = -17 \\ x + y - 2z = 5 \end{array} \right\}$$

Subtract the top equation from the bottom equation to eliminate x from the bottom equation.

$$\left. \begin{array}{l} x + 2y - z = 6 \\ -7y + 3z = -17 \\ -y - z = -1 \end{array} \right\}$$

Interchange the second and third equations.

$$\left. \begin{array}{l} x + 2y - z = 6 \\ -y - z = -1 \\ -7y + 3z = -17 \end{array} \right\}$$

Subtract $7 \times$ the middle equation from the bottom equation to eliminate y from the bottom equation.

$$\left. \begin{array}{l} x + 2y - z = 6 \\ -y - z = -1 \\ 10z = -10 \end{array} \right\}$$

Find z from the last equation, and substitute to find y in the second equation.	$\left.\begin{array}{r} x+2y-z=6 \\ y=2 \\ z=-1 \end{array}\right\}$

Use the values of z and y and substitute them in the first equation to find x.	$\left.\begin{array}{r} x=1 \\ y=2 \\ z=-1 \end{array}\right\}$

The arithmetic may be a little easier, but there is an extra stage of working.

Sometimes you may get zero entries in embarrassing places.

3 Solve the simultaneous equations
$$\begin{array}{r} 3y+2z=5 \\ x-2y=4 \\ x-3y+z=9 \end{array}$$

In this case there is no x in the first equation to use for the elimination. Interchange the first and second equations to help.

Interchange the first two equations.	$\left.\begin{array}{r} x-2y=4 \\ 3y+2z=5 \\ x-3y+z=9 \end{array}\right\}$

Subtract the top equation from the bottom equation to eliminate x from the bottom equation.	$\left.\begin{array}{r} x-2y=4 \\ 3y+2z=5 \\ -y+z=5 \end{array}\right\}$

Interchange the last two equations.	$\left.\begin{array}{r} x-2y=4 \\ -y+z=5 \\ 3y+2z=5 \end{array}\right\}$

Add $3 \times$ the middle equation to the bottom equation to eliminate y from the bottom equation.	$\left.\begin{array}{r} x - 2y \qquad = 4 \\ -y + z = 5 \\ 5z = 20 \end{array}\right\}$
Find z from the last equation, and substitute to find y in the second equation.	$\left.\begin{array}{r} x - 2y \qquad = 4 \\ y = -1 \\ z = 4 \end{array}\right\}$
Use the values of z and y and substitute them in the first equation to find x.	$\left.\begin{array}{r} x = 2 \\ y = -1 \\ z = 4 \end{array}\right\}$

Exercise 18

Solve the following sets of equations for x, y and z.

1 $\left.\begin{array}{r} x + y + z = 5 \\ -x - 2y + 2z = -5 \\ 2x + y - z = 4 \end{array}\right\}$
2 $\left.\begin{array}{r} x - 2y - z = 3 \\ x + y + z = 4 \\ 2x - y + z = 12 \end{array}\right\}$

3 $\left.\begin{array}{r} x + 3y - z = 15 \\ 2x - y - z = 1 \\ 3x + 2y + 10z = 4 \end{array}\right\}$
4 $\left.\begin{array}{r} x - y \qquad = 2 \\ y - z = 2 \\ x + \qquad z = 6 \end{array}\right\}$

5 $\left.\begin{array}{r} 3x - y - z = -8 \\ 2x + y + 2z = 1 \\ x - y + z = 2 \end{array}\right\}$
6 $\left.\begin{array}{r} 2x - y - z = 10 \\ x + y - z = 4 \\ 3x - y + 2z = 11 \end{array}\right\}$

7 $\left.\begin{array}{r} 8x + 4y - z = 3 \\ 2x + y - 2z = -1 \\ 3x + 2y + 3z = 4 \end{array}\right\}$
8 $\left.\begin{array}{r} x \qquad + 2z = -3 \\ x + y \qquad = 5 \\ y + z = 2 \end{array}\right\}$

9 $\left.\begin{array}{r} 2x + 3y + 4z = 16 \\ 3x - 2y + 3z = 8 \\ 4x + 2y - 2z = 14 \end{array}\right\}$
10 $\left.\begin{array}{r} 4x - 3y + 5z = -5 \\ 2x + 3y - 3z = 23 \\ 3x + 2y + z = 13 \end{array}\right\}$

19 Revision exercises

Revision exercise 1

1. Simplify $\dfrac{3x^{-2}z^2}{x^4 y^{-2}} \times \dfrac{x^2}{y^2}$.

2. Solve the equation $4^x = 0.2$.

3. Rationalise the denominator in the expression $\dfrac{\sqrt{3}+\sqrt{2}}{\sqrt{3}-\sqrt{2}}$.

4. Solve the simultaneous equations $7x + y = 25$ and $x^2 + y^2 = 25$.

5. Solve the inequality $\dfrac{1}{x} > 3$.

6. Find the values of k such that the equation $x^2 - 2kx + (3k - 2) = 0$ has equal roots.

Revision exercise 2

1. The last term of an arithmetic progression is 36 and the first term is 2. The sum is 893. Find the number of terms.

2. Express the sum $4 + 6 + 8 + \ldots + 38$ in Σ notation.

3. Find the remainder when $x^3 + 2x^2 + 3x + 4$ is divided by $x + 3$.

4. Use the method of equating coefficients to find the quotient and the remainder when $2x^2 - 5x - 4$ is divided by $x - 2$.

5. What is the effect of replacing the graph of $y = f(x)$ by the graph of $y = f(x + 2) + 2$.

6. Find the range of the function $f : \mathbf{R} \rightarrow \mathbf{R}$ given by $f(x) = x^2 - 4x + 2$.

Revision exercise 3

1. Let $f(x) = x^2$ and $g(x) = 2x - 3$. Find expressions for the functions $g(f(x))$ and $f(g(x))$.

2. Solve the simultaneous equations $x^2 - 2xy - y^2 = 14$ and $2x + 3y = 3$.

3. Simplify $\dfrac{4x^2 y}{2z^2 y^3} \div \dfrac{8^{-1} x^{-4} z^3}{x^{-3} y^{-2}}$.

4   The fourth term of an arithmetic progression is 7, and the eighth term is 19. Find the sum of the first 20 terms.

5   Express $\dfrac{x+8}{(x-1)(x+2)}$ in partial fractions.

6   Find the first four terms of the expansion $(1-2x)^{-\frac{1}{2}}$, and state the values of x for which the expansion is valid.

Revision exercise 4

1   A geometric progression has 12 as its second term and $-1\frac{1}{2}$ as its fifth term. Find its sum to infinity.

2   Express as a single logarithm to the base 10, $\log_{10} 5 + 2\log_{10} 2 - 1$.

3   Solve the simultaneous equations $\left.\begin{array}{l} x - 2y + z = 1 \\ 3x - 4y + z = 3 \\ 2x + 2y - 3z = 3 \end{array}\right\}$.

4   Solve the inequality $\dfrac{1}{x} > \dfrac{2}{x^2} - 1$.

5   Find the sum of the series $\displaystyle\sum_{r=1}^{100} r(r+1)(r+2)$.

6   Rationalise the denominator of the expression $\dfrac{\left(2+\sqrt{3}\right)^2}{1+\sqrt{3}}$.

Revision exercise 5

1   The equation $(k+1)x^2 - 6(3k-1)x + 18 = 0$ has no roots. Find the range of possible values of k.

2   The graph of $y = f(x)$ is reflected in the y-axis and stretched by a factor of 2 in the y-direction. Write down its new equation.

3   Solve the simultaneous equations $\left.\begin{array}{l} 3y + 2z = 8 \\ x + 2y - 3z = 1 \\ 4x - y + z = -1 \end{array}\right\}$.

4   The line $y = 2x + k$ touches the curve $y = x^2$. Find the value of k.

5   Express $\dfrac{1}{4+2\sqrt{2}}$ in the form $a - \sqrt{b}$.

6   Find the quotient and remainder when $2x^3 - 4x^2 + 3x - 1$ is divided by $x - 1$.

Revision exercise 6

1   The cubic expression $x^3 + ax^2 + x + b$ leaves a remainder of -4 when it is divided by $x - 1$ and a remainder of -2 when divided by $x - 2$. Find the values of a and b.

2   Find the inverse of the function $f(x) = 2x - 3$.

3   A banker invests £1000 at the beginning of each year at compound interest of 5%. How much will the banker have in total at the end of the 20th year?

4   Express $\dfrac{6 - 9x}{(x + 2)(x^2 + 2)}$ in partial fractions.

5   Find the sum $\displaystyle\sum_{r=1}^{n} (r + 1)(r - 2)$.

6   Find the first four terms of the expansion of $\dfrac{2 + 3x}{1 - x^2}$ in ascending powers of x.

Revision exercise 7

1   Find the first four terms of the binomial expansion of $\dfrac{1 + x}{1 - x}$.

2   Express $\dfrac{1 + 11x + 6x^2}{(1 - x)(1 + 2x)^2}$ in partial fractions.

3   Find the factors of $36x^3 + 21x^2 - 20x - 12$.

4   The equation $\dfrac{1 - 2x}{1 + x^2} = k$ has no roots. Find the possible values of k.

5   The arithmetic progression has a first term of 1059 and a common difference of -23. Find the number of terms such that the sum is negative for the first time.

6   Solve the simultaneous equations $\left. \begin{array}{r} y + z = 3 \\ x + y \quad = 3 \\ x \quad + z = 2 \end{array} \right\}$

20 Answers

Exercise 2, page 6

1	$6a^3$	**2**	$18a^3$
3	$12a^3$	**4**	2
5	3	**6**	5
7	4	**8**	4
9	$\frac{1}{4}$	**10**	$\frac{1}{27}$
11	3	**12**	$\frac{1}{3}$
13	$5a$	**14**	$\frac{2}{a}$
15	$\frac{1}{2a}$	**16**	8
17	2	**18**	16
19	$\frac{1}{100}$	**20**	$1\frac{1}{4}$
21	$\frac{3}{a^2}$	**22**	$\frac{1}{9a^2}$
23	9	**24**	$\frac{1}{a}$
25	9	**26**	2
27	9	**28**	9
29	$\frac{1}{3}$	**30**	0.2
31	$6a$	**32**	$\frac{3}{2}a$
33	$18a$	**34**	$\frac{1}{64}$
35	8	**36**	$\frac{1}{16}$
37	$\frac{1}{25}$	**38**	1
39	$\frac{1}{8}$	**40**	0.09
41	$\frac{6}{a}$	**42**	$\frac{2}{9a}$
43	$\frac{1}{8}$	**44**	$2\frac{1}{4}$
45	9	**46**	$\frac{1}{4}$
47	2	**48**	1
49	$\frac{1}{32}$	**50**	$\frac{2}{a^2}$

51 $\dfrac{6}{x^2}$ **52** 2

53 $\frac{27}{64}$ **54** $\dfrac{2}{a^3}$

55 $\dfrac{12a^4}{b}$ **56** $\dfrac{4a}{9b}$

57 $\frac{1}{5}$ **58** $\dfrac{15b}{a}$

59 $4x^5$ **60** $\frac{64}{27}$

61 $\dfrac{1}{a^2}$ **62** $\dfrac{1}{b}$

63 $\dfrac{1}{c^{\frac{2}{3}}}$ **64** $\dfrac{x}{y}$

65 $\dfrac{1}{xy}$ **66** $\dfrac{b^3}{a^2}$

67 $\dfrac{a}{b^3}$ **68** $\dfrac{1}{a^3b^3}$

69 $\dfrac{2}{x^{\frac{1}{2}}}$ **70** $\dfrac{3}{y^{\frac{2}{5}}}$

71 4   **72** 27

73 $\frac{1}{2}$ **74** $\frac{1}{3}$

75 3   **76** $\frac{1}{25}$

77 $\frac{1}{27}$ **78** $-\frac{1}{2}$

79 4   **80** 81

81 0.3   **82** $\frac{5}{6}$

83 $\frac{4}{3}$ **84** $\frac{2}{3}$

85 $\frac{1}{2}a^2$ **86** x^{-1}

87 $x^{-5}y^{-1}$ **88** $\frac{1}{2}x^{-\frac{1}{2}}y^4$

Exercise 3, page 11

1 2   **2** 3

3 2   **4** 4

5 2   **6** 3

7 −1   **8** 3

9 $1\frac{1}{2}$ **10** $\frac{2}{3}$

11	$-\frac{1}{2}$	**12**	$\frac{1}{2}$
13	$\frac{1}{3}$	**14**	$-1\frac{1}{2}$
15	$-\frac{1}{2}$	**16**	$-1\frac{1}{2}$
17	$-1\frac{1}{2}$	**18**	$-1\frac{1}{3}$
19	3	**20**	-2
21	$3p$	**22**	$2r$
23	$p+r$	**24**	$p+q+r$
25	$1-p$	**26**	$1-p+r$
27	$q-2p$	**28**	$2p+q-1$
29	$\log 12$	**30**	$\log\frac{4}{3}$
31	$\log 125$	**32**	$\log 5$
33	$\log\frac{1}{3}$	**34**	$\log 30$
35	1000	**36**	0.01
37	3	**38**	$1\frac{1}{2}$
39	2	**40**	$1\frac{1}{3}$
41	$\frac{1}{4}$	**42**	-1
43	$x=a^b$	**44**	$xy=a$
45	$ax=1$	**46**	$xy^2=a^3$
47	$x=yz$	**48**	$x^2=y^3z^4$
49	2.322	**50**	0.921
51	0.603	**52**	0.631
53	1.544	**54**	3.989
55	-1.585	**56**	-0.301
57	0.477	**58**	2.096
59	2.861	**60**	2.672
61	-0.092	**62**	0.139
63	-2.322	**64**	0.162

Exercise 4, page 17

1	$\sqrt{12}$	**2**	$\sqrt{18}$
3	$\sqrt{8}$	**4**	$\sqrt{27}$
5	$\sqrt{50}$	**6**	$\sqrt{45}$
7	$\sqrt{28}$	**8**	$\sqrt{96}$

9	$\sqrt{108}$	10	$\sqrt{125}$
11	$\sqrt{300}$	12	$\sqrt{90}$
13	$\sqrt{44}$	14	$\sqrt{72}$
15	$\sqrt{175}$	16	$\sqrt{216}$
17	$2\sqrt{5}$	18	$4\sqrt{2}$
19	$4\sqrt{3}$	20	$5\sqrt{3}$
21	$6\sqrt{2}$	22	$2\sqrt{6}$
23	$3\sqrt{7}$	24	$3\sqrt{6}$
25	$10\sqrt{2}$	26	$2\sqrt{21}$
27	$3\sqrt{11}$	28	$5\sqrt{6}$
29	$7\sqrt{2}$	30	$12\sqrt{2}$
31	$5\sqrt{2}$	32	4
33	6	34	$5\sqrt{6}$
35	6	36	48
37	$2\sqrt{2}$	38	$6\sqrt{5}$
39	$8\sqrt{6}$	40	$9\sqrt{3}$
41	28	42	60
43	60	44	$24\sqrt{10}$
45	$\frac{1}{2}\sqrt{2}$	46	$\sqrt{2}$
47	$3\sqrt{2}$	48	$2\sqrt{5}$
49	$\sqrt{2}$	50	$\frac{7}{2}\sqrt{6}$
51	$5\sqrt{3}$	52	$\frac{2}{5}\sqrt{5}$
53	$\frac{3}{7}\sqrt{7}$	54	$3\sqrt{7}$
55	$\sqrt{2}$	56	$\frac{4}{3}\sqrt{2}$
57	$\frac{1}{5}\sqrt{6}$	58	$\frac{3}{5}\sqrt{5}$
59	$2\sqrt{3}$	60	$\frac{5}{2}\sqrt{2}$
61	$3\sqrt{3}$	62	0
63	$\sqrt{7}$	64	$\sqrt{5}$
65	0	66	$12\sqrt{2}$
67	$2\sqrt{6}$	68	$2\sqrt{6}$
69	$7\sqrt{7}$	70	6
71	$\frac{1}{2}\sqrt{6}$	72	$\frac{11}{9}\sqrt{3}$
73	$\frac{9}{2}\sqrt{2}$	74	$2\sqrt{6}$

75 $2+\sqrt{3}$ **76** $2-\sqrt{3}$

77 $\sqrt{3}+\sqrt{2}$ **78** $\sqrt{3}-\sqrt{2}$

79 $\frac{1}{7}\left(11-6\sqrt{2}\right)$ **80** $13-9\sqrt{2}$

81 $\sqrt{5}+\frac{3}{2}\sqrt{2}$ **82** $23-5\sqrt{21}$

83 $\frac{3}{2}\sqrt{5}+\frac{3}{2}\sqrt{3}$ **84** $\frac{2}{3}-\frac{1}{6}\sqrt{10}$

85 3 **86** $\sqrt{3}-1$

87 $2+\sqrt{3}$ **88** $\frac{1}{3}$

89 $\dfrac{a+b-2\sqrt{ab}}{a-b}$ **90** $2n+1+2\sqrt{n(n+1)}$

Exercise 5, page 23

1 $x=1,\ y=1$ and $x=1\frac{2}{3},\ y=2\frac{1}{3}$ **2** $x=5,\ y=-3$ and $x=-3,\ y=5$

3 $x=3,\ y=-1$ and $x=-3,\ y=1$ **4** $x=1,\ y=\frac{2}{3}$ (repeated)

5 $x=3,\ y=-2$ and $x=\frac{1}{3},\ y=6$ **6** $x=6,\ y=-3$

7 $x=5,\ y=-2$ **8** $x=2,\ y=-1$

9 $x=5,\ y=-3$ **10** $x=3,\ y=4$

11 $x=0,\ y=\frac{1}{2}$ and $x=1,\ y=3$ **12** $x=2,y=1$ and $x=-1\frac{1}{3},y=-1\frac{1}{2}$

13 $x=4,\ y=6$ and $x=-2,\ y=-6$ **14** $x=4,\ y=-1$ and $x=8,\ y=-3$

15 $x=7,\ y=-2$ and $x=-4,\ y=3\frac{1}{2}$ **16** $x=2,\ y=-9$ and $x=-1,y=-12$

17 $x=-1,\ y=3$ and $x=1\frac{1}{2},\ y=-2$ **18** $x=6,y=1$ and $x=-2\frac{1}{2},y=-2\frac{2}{5}$

19 $x=-1,\ y=1$ and $x=3,\ y=-5$ **20** $x=-6,\ y=1$ and $x=-1\frac{1}{2},\ y=4$

21 $x=4,\ y=2$ and $x=-2,\ y=-\frac{2}{5}$ **22** $x=-3,\ y=5$ and $x=2,\ y=-2\frac{1}{2}$

23 $x=2,\ y=-3$ and $x=3,\ y=-5$ **24** $x=2,\ y=3$

25 $x=4,\ y=1$ and $x=-5,\ y=-3\frac{1}{2}$ **26** $x=3,y=-2$ and $x=-5,\ y=-7\frac{1}{3}$

27 $x=15,\ y=12$ and $x=12,\ y=10$ **28** $x=1,\ y=-1$ and $x=2\frac{1}{2},\ y=-3$

Exercise 6, page 28

1 $x<2$ or $x>5$ **2** $-2<x<5$

3 $-3<x<-2$ **4** $x<-2$ or $x>5$

5 $x<-6$ or $x>6$ **6** $-10<x<10$

7 $-2<x<3$ **8** $x<-1$ or $x>4$

9 $x\leq-4$ or $x\geq4$ **10** $x<-3$ or $x>4$

11	$-6 \leq x \leq 2$	**12**	$x \leq -4$ or $x \geq \frac{1}{2}$
13	$-1\frac{1}{2} < x < 2$	**14**	$x \leq -2\frac{1}{2}$ or $x \geq 1\frac{1}{2}$
15	$-1 \leq x \leq 0$	**16**	$x = 1$
17	$x < 0$ or $x > 3$	**18**	$0 < x \leq 2$
19	$x < -3$ or $x > 0$	**20**	$0 < x \leq \frac{1}{6}$
21	$-4 < x < 0$	**22**	$x < -1\frac{1}{2}$ or $x > 0$
23	$\frac{1}{2} < x < 1$	**24**	$x < -1\frac{1}{2}$ or $x > 1\frac{1}{3}$
25	$x < 0$	**26**	$-2 < x < 0.4$
27	$x < \frac{1}{4}$	**28**	$x \leq \frac{1}{2}$ or $x \geq 2\frac{1}{2}$
29	$-1 \leq x \leq 2\frac{1}{3}$	**30**	$-1\frac{1}{3} \leq x \leq 2$
31	No values of x	**32**	All values of x

Exercise 7, page 32

1	No roots	**2**	2 roots
3	1 root	**4**	No roots
5	1 root	**6**	2 roots
7	No roots	**8**	2 roots
9	$k < 1\frac{1}{8}$	**10**	$k < 2$
11	$k < -8$ or $k > 8$	**12**	$k < -\sqrt{24}$, $k > \sqrt{24}$
13	$k < 4$	**14**	All values of k except $k = 1$.
15	$k = 1\frac{1}{8}$	**16**	$k = 1$ or $k = -3$
17	$k = \frac{1}{3}$	**18**	$k = 3$ or $k = 1\frac{1}{4}$
19	$k = 3$	**20**	$k = -1$ or $k = 7$
21	$k = \pm 8$	**22**	$k = \pm 1$
23	$k = \pm 1$	**24**	$k = \frac{1}{2}$ or $k = 4$
25	No value of k	**26**	$k = -1$ or $k = -5$

27 If you attempt to find k, you find it has to satisfy the equation $k^2 = -4$, so no such k exists.

Exercise 8, page 38

1	1, 1	**2**	Not an AP
3	a, a	**4**	$2, -3\frac{1}{2}$

5	$29, 49, 2n-1$	6	$-23, -43, 7-2n$
7	$-44, -4, 4n-104$	8	$-47, -82, \frac{11}{2}-\frac{7}{2}n$
9	$32, 3n+5$	10	$4-\frac{3}{2}n, \frac{5}{2}-3n$
11	The 144th term	12	The 101st term
13	The 62nd term	14	The $(2n)$th term
15	$a=-29, d=9$	16	$a=4, d=-3$
17	30	18	42
19	7500	20	$a=10, d=0$
21	£1,024,000	22	n^2
23	14	24	59
25	$61, -\frac{14}{23}$	26	$-48, 50$

Exercise 9, page 45

1	$1, 2$	2	Not a GP
3	$a, 2a$	4	$8, -2$
5	$1, 1$	6	$a, -1$
7	$512, 131\,072, \frac{1}{2}\times4^{n-1}=2^{2n-3}$	8	$1\,000\,000, 10^{10}, 10^n$
9	$-\frac{3}{16}, -\frac{3}{256}, (-1)^{n-1}\times3\times2^{2-n}$	10	$-a^6, -a^{10}, (-1)^{n-1}a^n$
11	5×1.6^n	12	$(-1)^n\times\left(\frac{1}{2}\right)^{n-2}, -1\times\left(\frac{1}{2}\right)^{2n-1}$
13	The 11th term	14	The 13th term
15	The 13th term	16	The $(2n)$th term
17	$r=\pm\sqrt{2}, a=4$	18	$a=2, r=-3$ or $a=8, r=-\frac{3}{2}$
19	20	20	19
21	4	22	$\frac{2}{3}$
23	$\frac{14}{111}$	24	£2 415 995.48
25	$y=\frac{1}{2}x^2$	26	$2\frac{2}{3}$
27	16		

Exercise 10, page 53

Your answers may differ from the given answer and still be correct. If that happens try to reconcile the two answers. If you cannot do that, seek advice. In some cases alternative answers are given.

1 $\displaystyle\sum_{r=1}^{4}(r+1)$ or $\displaystyle\sum_{r=2}^{5}r$

2 $\displaystyle\sum_{r=1}^{4}(r+1)^2$ or $\displaystyle\sum_{r=2}^{5}r^2$

3 $\displaystyle\sum_{r=1}^{10}(2r)^2$

4 $\displaystyle\sum_{r=1}^{9}(2r+2)^3$ or $\displaystyle\sum_{r=2}^{10}(2r)^3$

5 $\displaystyle\sum_{r=1}^{n-1}\frac{1}{r+1}$ or $\displaystyle\sum_{r=2}^{n}\frac{1}{r}$

6 $\displaystyle\sum_{r=1}^{n}\frac{(-1)^{r+1}}{r^2}$

7 $\displaystyle\sum_{r=1}^{2n+1}\frac{(-1)^{r+1}}{r}$

8 $\displaystyle\sum_{r=1}^{100}\frac{(-1)^{r+1}}{\sqrt{r}}$

9 $\displaystyle\sum_{r=n+1}^{2n}r^2$

10 $\displaystyle\sum_{r=1}^{n}\frac{(-1)^{r+1}}{n+r}$

11 $3+4+5$

12 $\dfrac{1}{1}+\dfrac{1}{2}+\dfrac{1}{3}+\dfrac{1}{4}+\dfrac{1}{5}+\dfrac{1}{6}$

13 $1+1+1$

14 $a+(a+1)+(a+2)+\ldots+b$

15 $\dfrac{1}{8}+\dfrac{1}{10}+\dfrac{1}{12}+\dfrac{1}{14}+\dfrac{1}{16}$

16 $n^3+(n+1)^3+\ldots+(2n)^3$

17 $2^2-3^2+4^2-5^2+6^2$

18 $-2^2+3^2-4^2+5^2-6^2$

19 $(2n+3)^3+\ldots+(2(2n+1)+1)^3$

20 $(-1)^n\left(9^3+11^3+13^3+15^3+17^3\right)$

21 55

22 2870

23 216 225

24 65

25 168

26 11 480

27 3310

28 24 680

29 770

30 1 353 400

31 214 200

32 18 980

33 $\frac{1}{2}n(3n+1)$

34 $\frac{4}{3}n(2n+1)(4n+1)$

35 $\frac{1}{3}n(2n+1)(2n-1)$

36 n^2

37 $\frac{1}{4}n^2(n-1)^2$

38 $\frac{1}{4}n^2(3n+1)(5n+3)$

39 $\frac{3}{2}n(n+1)(2n+1)$

40 $n^2\left(2n^2-1\right)$

Exercise 11, page 58

1	0	**2**	-4
3	5	**4**	1
5	4	**6**	16
7	0	**8**	12
9	18	**10**	-1
11	3	**12**	9
13	0	**14**	0
15	12	**16**	$-\frac{1}{2}$
17	$13\frac{1}{2}$	**18**	$-28\frac{1}{2}$
19	$14\frac{1}{2}$	**20**	$\frac{4}{9}$
21	$2\frac{2}{9}$	**22**	-2
23	$(x-1)(x+2)(x+3)$	**24**	$(a+1)^2(a-2)$
25	$(d-2)(d+3)(d-4)$	**26**	$(m-3)(m+3)(m+4)$
27	$(c+2)(c-3)^2$	**28**	$(u+2)(u^2+u+1)$
29	$(n-3)(n^2+2n+3)$	**30**	$(y-1)(y+3)(2y-1)$
31	$(x+2)(x-3)(2x+3)$	**32**	$(m-2)(m+4)(m-7)$
33	$(n-1)^2(n+2)$	**34**	$(a-2)(a+2)(a+3)$
35	$(b+2)(b+3)(b-5)$	**36**	$(z-2)(2z-3)(3z+2)$
37	$a=-5, 2x^2+x-2$	**38**	$b=-2, 26$
39	$(x-1)$ and $(x-2)$	**40**	$a=-11, b=-9, (x-1)$ and $(x+3)$
41	$a=6, b=19, 3x+2$	**42**	$a=3, b=-4$
43	$2x^2-5x-3$	**44**	$a=2, b=1, c=-5$
45	$x-2$	**46**	$(x+1)$ and $(x-5)$

Exercise 12, page 64

1	$4x-3$	**2**	$4x-3$
3	$2x-3$	**4**	$2x-9$
5	$3x-2$	**6**	$3x+4$
7	a^2+a-1	**8**	m^2-m+2
9	x^2+2x-4, rem. 2	**10**	u^2-2u+3, rem. -4
11	$m^2-3mn-2n^2$	**12**	$x^2+2xy-y^2$

13 $b^2 + 2bc - 3c^2$, rem. $3c^3$ **14** $a^2 - 3ad + 2d^2$

15 $3x^2 - 2x - 4$, rem. -2 **16** $3y^2 - 4y + 6$, rem. -3

17 $a - 2b$ **18** $2m - u$

19 $3h^2 + 4hk - 2k^2$ **20** $2m^2 + 5mn - 3n^2$

21 $3b - 2$, rem. -3 **22** $3a - 1$, rem. 4

23 $m^2 + mn + n^2$ **24** $m + n$

25 $3u - 4v$ **26** $4m - 5n$

27 $2x + 1$ and $x + 3$ **28** $2y - 1$ and $2y + 3$

29 $z + 1$ and $2z - 1$ **30** $2x + 1$ and $3x - 1$

31 $3y - 2$ and $2y + 5$ **32** $3z - 4$ and $2z + 1$

33 $3x - 4$ and $2x + 3$ **34** $3y - 5$ and $2y - 3$

35 $x - 2y$ and $x - 3y$ **36** $3y + 2x$ and $y - 3x$

37 $A = 1, B = -2, C = 0, D = -4$ **38** $A = 1, B = 2, C = -1, D = -4$

39 $A = 2, B = 3, C = 8, D = 30$ **40** $A = 1, B = -1, C = 1, D = 2$

41 $A = 2, B = -2, C = 2, D = -3$ **42** $A = 2\frac{1}{2}, B = \frac{3}{4}, C = 1\frac{3}{8}, D = -2\frac{5}{8}$

43 $A = 5, B = 4, C = 6, D = 2$ **44** $A = 1, B = 0, C = -2, D = 11$

45 $A = 2, B = 3, C = 10, D = 43$ **46** $A = 1, B = -3, C = 4, D = 24$

47 $A = 3, B = -2, C = 5, D = -7$ **48** $A = -5, B = 3, C = -2, D = 12$

Exercise 13, page 69

1 Either a translation of 4 units in the y-direction, or a translation of -2 units in the x-direction.

2 Either a translation of -6 units in the y-direction, or a translation of 2 units in the x-direction.

3 A translation of 3 units in the y-direction.

4 A translation of -3 units in the x-direction.

5 Either a stretch of factor 4 in the y-direction, or a translation of -2 units in the x-direction.

6 Either a stretch of factor 4 in the y-direction, or a stretch of factor $\frac{1}{2}$ in the x-direction.

7 A translation of 2 units in the x-direction.

8 There are many possibilities, but the simplest is a translation of $\frac{1}{2}\pi$ units in the x-direction.

9 $y = f(x) + 3$

10 $y = f(x + 2)$

11 $y = f(x) - 4$

12 $y = f(x - 3) + 4$

13 $y = 4f(x)$

14 $y = 4f(x + 2)$

15 $y = 2f(x) + 1$

16 $y = 3f\left(\dfrac{x}{4}\right)$

17 A translation of 2 units in the *y*-direction followed by a translation of -1 unit in the *x*-direction, or vice versa.

18 A stretch of factor 2 in the *y*-direction followed by a translation of 1 unit in the *y*-direction.

19 A translation of 1 unit in the *x*-direction followed by a translation of 3 units in the *y*-direction , or vice versa.

20 A translation of $\frac{1}{3}\pi$ units in the *x*-direction followed by a stretch of factor 3 in the *y*-direction, or vice versa.

21

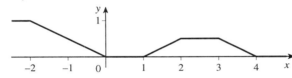

22

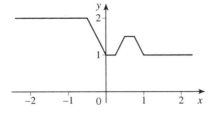

23

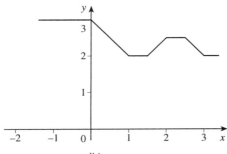

24

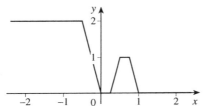

Exercise 14, page 75

1 f is both one to one and onto. The range of f is Y.

2 f is not one to one because $f(a) = f(b)$ and not onto because no element maps to x. The range of f is $\{y\}$.

3 The range is $-1 \le y \le 1$.

4 $f(x) = 2^x$ is one to one but not onto. Each element of the domain maps to just one element of the co-domain, but no element maps to 0 of the co-domain. The range of this function is $x > 0$.

5 $f(x) = x^3 - x$ is an example of a function which is onto but not one to one. Every element of **R** is the image of some element of **R** since it is always possible to solve the equation $x^3 - x = c$. However, it is not one to one because $f(0) = f(1) = 0$.

6 A function. The range is $x \ge 0$.

7 A function. The range is **R**.

8 Not a function, because it is not defined for $x = 0$.

9 A function. The range is $-1 \le x \le 1$.

10 Not a function, because it is not defined for $x = \frac{1}{2}\pi$.

11 A function. The range is $x > 0$.

12 Not a function, because it is not defined for $x = -1$.

13 A function. The range is $\mathbf{R}$.

14 A function. The range is the set $\mathbf{Z}$ of integers.

15 Not a function, because there is no smallest real number greater than a given number.

16 $1 \le x \le 2$

17 $\{x \in \mathbf{R} : x > 0\}$, $\mathbf{R}$

18 $\{x \in \mathbf{R} : x \le 1\}$, $\{y \in \mathbf{R} : y \ge 0\}$

19 $\{x \in \mathbf{R} : x \ne 1\}$, $\{y \in \mathbf{R} : y \ne 0\}$

20 $\{x \in \mathbf{R} : x \ne 1, x \ne -1\}$, $\{y \in \mathbf{R} : y > 0, y < -1\}$

21 Odd

22 Neither even nor odd

23 Odd

24 Even

Exercise 15, page 79

1 0, 3, $gf(x) = 4x^2 - 12x + 8$

2 2, $\frac{1}{5}$, $fg(x) = \dfrac{1}{4x^2 + 1}$, 0

3 $fg(x) = x$, $gf(x) = x$; they are inverse

4 $gf(x) = 2\sin\left(\frac{1}{2}\pi x\right)$, $fg(x) = \sin(\pi x)$; x is an even integer

5 $f^{-1}(x) = 2 - x$

6 $f^{-1}(x) = \frac{2}{3}(1 - 2x)$

7 $f^{-1}(x) = (x + 2)^{\frac{1}{3}}$

8 $f^{-1}(x) = \frac{1}{8}(x - 3)^3$

9 $B = \{x \in \mathbf{R} : x \ne -1\}$, $f^{-1}(x) = \dfrac{1}{x + 1}$

10 $k = 0$, $f^{-1} : A \rightarrow A$ such that $f^{-1}(x) = x^2$

11 $f(x) = \cos x$ is neither one to one, nor onto. $A = \{x \in \mathbf{R} : 0 \le x \le \pi\}$, $B = \{y \in \mathbf{R} : -1 \le y \le 1\}$

12 $f(x) = \tan x$ is not one to one. $A = \left\{x \in \mathbf{R} : -\frac{1}{2}\pi \le x \le \frac{1}{2}\pi\right\}$, $B = \mathbf{R}$

Exercise 16, page 86

1 $A = 3, B = 2$ **2** $A = 2, B = 4$

3 $A = 1, B = -2$ **4** $A = 2, B = 3$

5 $\dfrac{1}{(3-x)} - \dfrac{1}{(x+3)}$ **6** $\dfrac{2}{(x-2)} + \dfrac{1}{(x+1)}$

7 $\dfrac{3}{(x-1)} - \dfrac{1}{(x+2)}$ **8** $\dfrac{3}{(x+4)} - \dfrac{2}{(x+3)}$

9 $\dfrac{6}{(x-2)} - \dfrac{12}{(x-1)}$ **10** $\dfrac{3}{(x-3)} - \dfrac{2}{(2x-1)}$

11 $\dfrac{1}{(3x-2)} - \dfrac{1}{(3x+2)}$ **12** $\dfrac{1}{(3x-2)} + \dfrac{1}{(3x+2)}$

13 $\dfrac{1}{(x-2)} + \dfrac{1}{(x+2)} - \dfrac{1}{(x+1)}$ **14** $\dfrac{1}{(x-3)} + \dfrac{2}{(2x+3)} - \dfrac{4}{(2x+1)}$

15 $\dfrac{2}{(2x+7)} - \dfrac{1}{(x+5)} + \dfrac{2}{(2x+1)}$ **16** $\dfrac{2}{(x+3)} - \dfrac{1}{(x-4)} - \dfrac{1}{(x+1)}$

17 $\dfrac{2}{(x+1)} - \dfrac{1}{\left(x^2+4\right)}$ **18** $\dfrac{3}{(x+2)} - \dfrac{2x-3}{\left(x^2+5\right)}$

19 $\dfrac{2x+1}{\left(x^2+x+2\right)} - \dfrac{3}{(x+5)}$ **20** $\dfrac{4x-3}{\left(x^2+4x+5\right)} - \dfrac{9}{(3x-2)}$

21 $\dfrac{2}{(x-2)} - \dfrac{x+2}{(x+1)^2}$ **22** $\dfrac{2}{(2x-1)} + \dfrac{x-1}{(x+3)^2}$

23 $\dfrac{1}{(x-1)} + \dfrac{2x-8}{(x-2)^2}$ **24** $\dfrac{2}{(x-1)} + \dfrac{2x+1}{(x+1)^2}$

25 $\dfrac{3}{(2x+1)} - \dfrac{4x+11}{(x+2)^2}$ **26** $\dfrac{14x-10}{(2x-1)^2} - \dfrac{4}{(2x+3)}$

27 $\dfrac{2}{(2x-1)} + \dfrac{16x+9}{(4x+3)^2}$ **28** $\dfrac{2}{(2x-1)} - \dfrac{16x+15}{(4x+3)^2}$

29 $\dfrac{2}{(x-2)} - \dfrac{1}{(x+1)} - \dfrac{1}{(x+1)^2}$ **30** $\dfrac{1}{(x+3)} + \dfrac{2}{(2x-1)} - \dfrac{4}{(x+3)^2}$

31 $\dfrac{2}{(x-2)} + \dfrac{1}{(x-1)} - \dfrac{4}{(x-2)^2}$ **32** $\dfrac{2}{(x+1)} + \dfrac{2}{(x-1)} - \dfrac{1}{(x+1)^2}$

33 $\dfrac{3}{(2x+1)} - \dfrac{4}{(x+2)} - \dfrac{3}{(x+2)^2}$ **34** $\dfrac{7}{(2x-1)} - \dfrac{4}{(2x+3)} - \dfrac{3}{(2x-1)^2}$

3 5 $\dfrac{2}{(2x-1)}+\dfrac{4}{(4x+3)}-\dfrac{3}{(4x+3)^2}$ **3 6** $\dfrac{2}{(2x-1)}-\dfrac{4}{(4x+3)}-\dfrac{3}{(4x+3)^2}$

Exercise 17, page 95

1	$1+4x+6x^2+4x^3+x^4$	**2**	$1+2y+y^2$
3	$1+6x+12x^2+8x^3$	**4**	$1+12x+54x^2+108x^3+81x^4$
5	$4+12x+9x^2$	**6**	$27+54x+36x^2+8x^3$
7	$32+80y+80y^2+40y^3+10y^4+y^5$	**8**	$1-4x+6x^2-4x^3+x^4$
9	$1-6x+12x^2-8x^3$	**1 0**	$64-48x+12x^2-x^3$
1 1	$256+768x+864x^2+432x^3+81x^4$	**1 2**	$27-54x+36x^2-8x^3$
1 3	$8-6x+\frac{3}{2}x^2-\frac{1}{8}x^3$	**1 4**	$2x^2+2\sqrt{2}xy+y^2$
1 5	$x^3+6x^2y+12xy^2+8y^3$		
1 6	$81x^4-216x^3y+216x^2y^2-96xy^3+16y^4$		
1 7	36	**1 8**	165
1 9	1792	**2 0**	672
2 1	79 200 000	**2 2**	−2 099 520
2 3	−1 548 288	**2 4**	180
2 5	$1-2x+3x^2,\ -1<x<1$	**2 6**	$1+\frac{3}{2}x+\frac{3}{8}x^2,\ -1<x<1$
2 7	$1-3x+6x^2,\ -1<x<1$	**2 8**	$1+\frac{2}{3}x-\frac{1}{9}x^2,\ -1<x<1$
2 9	$1-\frac{1}{2}x+\frac{3}{8}x^2,\ -1<x<1$	**3 0**	$1-\frac{1}{4}x+\frac{5}{32}x^2,\ -1<x<1$
3 1	$1+x+x^2,\ -1<x<1$	**3 2**	$1+\frac{1}{3}x+\frac{2}{9}x^2,\ -1<x<1$
3 3	$1-4x+12x^2,\ -\frac{1}{2}<x<\frac{1}{2}$	**3 4**	$1+\frac{9}{2}x+\frac{27}{8}x^2,\ -\frac{1}{3}<x<\frac{1}{3}$
3 5	$1+\frac{3}{2}x+\frac{3}{2}x^2,\ -2<x<2$	**3 6**	$1-\frac{8}{3}x-\frac{16}{9}x^2,\ -\frac{1}{4}<x<\frac{1}{4}$
3 7	$1-\frac{3}{2}x+\frac{27}{8}x^2,\ -\frac{1}{3}<x<\frac{1}{3}$	**3 8**	$1-\frac{1}{12}x+\frac{5}{288}x^2,\ -3<x<3$
3 9	$1+2x+4x^2,\ -\frac{1}{2}<x<\frac{1}{2}$	**4 0**	$1+\frac{4}{3}x+\frac{32}{9}x^2,\ -\frac{1}{4}<x<\frac{1}{4}$
4 1	$a=\frac{1}{4},\ b=\frac{3}{2}$	**4 2**	$a=\frac{1}{3},\ b=-\frac{5}{3}$
4 3	$a=2,\ b=\frac{1}{2}$	**4 4**	$a=\frac{\sqrt{3}}{3},\ b=\frac{2}{3}$
4 5	$a=4,\ b=\frac{3}{8}$	**4 6**	$a=27,\ b=-\frac{2}{9}$
4 7	$a=\frac{1}{9},\ b=-2$	**4 8**	$a=\frac{1}{8},\ b=-\frac{3}{4}$
4 9	$\frac{1}{4}-\frac{3}{4}x+\frac{27}{16}x^2,\ -\frac{2}{3}<x<\frac{2}{3}$	**5 0**	$\frac{1}{3}+\frac{5}{9}x+\frac{25}{27}x^2,\ -\frac{3}{5}<x<\frac{3}{5}$
5 1	$2+\frac{1}{2}x-\frac{1}{16}x^2,\ -2<x<2$	**5 2**	$\frac{\sqrt{3}}{3}-\frac{\sqrt{3}}{9}x+\frac{\sqrt{3}}{18}x^2,\ -\frac{3}{2}<x<\frac{3}{2}$
5 3	$4+x-\frac{1}{16}x^2,\ -\frac{8}{3}<x<\frac{8}{3}$	**5 4**	$27-9x+\frac{1}{2}x^2,\ -\frac{9}{2}<x<\frac{9}{2}$
5 5	$\frac{1}{9}+\frac{5}{9}x+\frac{16}{9}x^2,\ -\frac{1}{2}<x<\frac{1}{2}$	**5 6**	$\frac{1}{8}+\frac{9}{64}x+\frac{7}{1024}x^2,\ -\frac{4}{3}<x<\frac{4}{3}$

57 $1 + 3x + 4x^2, -\frac{1}{3} < x < \frac{1}{3}$

58 $1 - \frac{5}{2}x - \frac{9}{8}x^2, -\frac{1}{5} < x < \frac{1}{5}$

59 $1 + 3x + 6x^2, -\frac{1}{2} < x < \frac{1}{2}$

60 $1 - 2x + 3x^2, -\frac{2}{3} < x < \frac{2}{3}$

61 $1 - x + 3x^2, -\frac{1}{2} < x < \frac{1}{2}$

62 $\frac{1}{2} + \frac{5}{4}x + \frac{19}{8}x^2, -\frac{1}{2} < x < \frac{1}{2}$

63 $\frac{1}{2} + x + \frac{1}{16}x^2, -2 < x < 2$

64 $\frac{1}{2} - \frac{5}{2}x + \frac{51}{8}x^2, -\frac{1}{2} < x < \frac{1}{2}$

Exercise 18, page 100

1 $x = 1, y = 3, z = 1$

2 $x = 2, y = -3, z = 5$

3 $x = 2, y = 4, z = -1$

4 $x = 5, y = 3, z = 1$

5 $x = -2, y = -1, z = 3$

6 $x = 4, y = -1, z = -1$

7 $x = 1, y = -1, z = 1$

8 $x = 1, y = 4, z = -2$

9 $x = 3, y = 2, z = 1$

10 $x = 4, y = 2, z = -3$

Revision exercise 1, page 101

1 $3x^{-4}z^2$

2 $-1.1609\ldots$

3 $5 + 2\sqrt{6}$

4 $x = 3, y = 4$ or $x = 4, y = -3$

5 $0 < x < \frac{1}{3}$

6 $k = 1$ or 2

Revision exercise 2, page 101

1 47

2 $\displaystyle\sum_{r=2}^{19} 2r$ or $\displaystyle\sum_{r=1}^{18} 2(r+1)$

3 -14

4 Quotient $2x - 1$, remainder -6

5 It translates the graph of $y = f(x)$ by -2 units in the x-direction and by 2 units in the y-direction.

6 $\{y \in \mathbf{R} : y \geq -2\}$

Revision exercise 3, page 101

1 $g(f(x)) = 2x^2 - 3$, $f(g(x)) = (2x - 3)^2$

2 $x = 3$, $y = -1$ or $x = -\frac{45}{17}$, $y = \frac{47}{17}$

3 $16x^3 y^{-4} z^{-5}$

4 530

5 $\dfrac{3}{x-1} - \dfrac{2}{x+2}$

6 $1 + x + \frac{3}{2}x^2 + \frac{5}{2}x^3$, $-\frac{1}{2} < x < \frac{1}{2}$

Revision exercise 4, page 102

1 -16

2 $\log_{10} 2$

3 $x = 2$, $y = 1$, $z = 1$

4 $x < -2$ or $x > 1$

5 $26\,527\,650$

6 $\dfrac{5 + 3\sqrt{3}}{2}$

Revision exercise 5, page 102

1 $-\frac{1}{9} < k < 1$

2 $y = 2f(-x)$

3 $x = 0$, $y = 2$, $z = 1$

4 -1

5 $\frac{1}{2} - \sqrt{\frac{1}{8}}$

6 Quotient $2x^2 - 3x + 1$, remainder 0

Revision exercise 6, page 102

1 $a = -2$, $b = -4$

2 $f^{-1}(x) = \frac{1}{2}(x + 3)$

3 £35,719.25

4   $\dfrac{4}{x+2} - \dfrac{4x+1}{x^2+2}$

5   $\frac{1}{3}n\left(n^2 - 7\right)$

6   $2 + 3x + 2x^2 + 3x^3$

Revision exercise 7, page 103

1   $1 + 2x + 2x^2 + 2x^3$

2   $\dfrac{2}{1-x} + \dfrac{1}{1+2x} - \dfrac{2}{(1+2x)^2}$

3   $(2 + 3x)(3x + 2)(4x - 3)$

4   $k > \frac{1}{2} + \frac{1}{2}\sqrt{5}$ or $k < \frac{1}{2} - \frac{1}{2}\sqrt{5}$

5   94 terms

6   $x = 1,\, y = 2,\, z = 1$

Index